COLLECTORS FOR TRAINS, TRAMS AND TROLLEYS

David Hartland

"Man is born to trouble as the sparks fly upwards"
Book of Job, Chapter 5 Verse 7.

This is the history of the company presently known as
Brecknell, Willis & Co (Established 1928)
Previously known as

Henry Brecknell (Established 1854),
Henry Brecknell and Sons, (Established 1858)
Henry Brecknell, Sons and Munro (Established 1894)
Brecknell, Munro & Rogers Limited (incorporated 1904)

Cover pictures:
Front: see 6.12 on page 47
Rear: see 4.3 on page 20

Published May 2004

ISBN 1 904474 29 2

Design David Pede

Published by
Middleton Press
Easebourne Lane
Midhurst, West Sussex
GU29 9AZ
Tel: 01730 813169
Fax: 01730 812601
Email: info@middletonpress.co.uk
www.middletonpress.co.uk

Printed & bound by Biddles Ltd,Kings Lynn

Contents

Introduction and Acknowledgements

When I joined Brecknell, Willis in 1984 I was aware that there was a history here, but details were scarce. A few notes had been established by the then Managing Director, Ken McQueen, but this left great swathes of time undocumented. Tony Hobbs, Managing Director 1986-1996, encouraged Norman Hollingsworth to research the history concentrating on Brecknell family sources and Companies House. Norman died in 1993, but in writing this book I have drawn heavily on the formal detail of dates, names and places which he had documented so thoroughly. I am sorry he did not live to see his efforts come to fruition, on this, the 150th anniversary of the Company.

In the early years, a good record of achievements was kept by the Company photographer, with many hundreds of glass plates faithfully recording the products. When the organisation moved to Chard in 1938 to avoid the bombing in Bristol, it was unfortunate that the sales office remained, for on the night of 3rd January 1941 the Bristol office suffered a direct hit and was destroyed, and with it the entire collection of glass plates. What remains, therefore, from the pre-war period is a small number of prints which have been collected from various sources and copied. To these, and more recent photographs, I have added captions with information pieced together from a number of sources. These pictures tell the real history - the technical and human stories which do not appear in the balance sheets or the Directors' reports. I have enjoyed the exercise, and have tried hard to ensure accuracy, but there is the chance that errors have crept in and for this I apologise in advance.

I must express my thanks to all those who have helped with photographs and information. Particular thanks go to the following:
James Atyeo, Jim Atherton, Sandy Barley, Chris Beer, Roy Beer, Michael Brown, Ashley Bruce, Peter Davey, Jeff Farley, Audrey Follett, Bob Hall, Norman Henley, the late Norman Hollingsworth, Tony Hobbs, Mary Hooper, Ken McQueen, Mike Mammatt, Vic Mitchell, Keith Phillips, the late J.H.Price, the late Peter Stevens, Gabriel Summers, David Wheadon, Tony White, Bryan Woodriff and Don Woodsell.

I must also thank my wife, Rachel, for her patience and encouragement over several years as I have brought (this) work home with me!

David Hartland, May 2004.

Chapter 1 - Brassfounders and Hydraulics.

England in 1826 was dramatically different from today. Only a few years previously had the threat of French invasion been removed. The industrial revolution was underway, but was yet to make much impression on the majority of the population. Science was a branch of philosophy; engineering was either military or civil, and electricity was merely a scientist's interesting laboratory experiment. The Stockton and Darlington Railway had been opened the year before, but only as a local colliery line, and any ideas of a national railway system were many years away. For the present, transport systems depended on the horse, or canalboat; or for most people on foot.

It was into this environment that Henry (also known as Job) Brecknell was born in Hotwells Road, Bristol, at home. His father Samuel was a tailor, and his mother Catherine kept the family house. Young Henry must have spent some of his childhood playing in the docks area and no doubt the sights, sounds and smells of the Bristol docks excited him, and this, with the forward-looking mood of the time, encouraged him into an engineering career. By the age of 28 he was planning his own business, and that same year, 1854, he established the company of Henry Brecknell - Brassfounder at 28 Lawrence Hill. The premises had a foundry at the rear, and living quarters above. His marriage to Hannah produced two sons, Henry and Edwin, and in 1858 the firm's name was changed to Henry Brecknell and Sons. The products were brass castings and stampings aimed at the water hydraulic industry. The Company was clearly at the forefront of developments, and Henry Brecknell (senior) had several patents to his credit. One major example was for a design of water valve which achieved the seal by the use of an india-rubber washer to close off the inlet orifice. This style of water valve became widely used, and is the basis of all modern household water taps.

Brecknell's business increased, and became an important player in the world of hydraulics, which in the mid-19th century was the most important system of power transmission, driving everything from factory machinery to lifting bridges. Perhaps the most famous hydraulic bridge of the period was London's Tower Bridge, which was completed in 1894, with the bridge decks being powered by water pressure.

We know little more about the founder of this interesting company, except his death, which occurred on 16th July 1880, at the early age of 54. The two sons Henry and Edwin were left to carry on with the business.

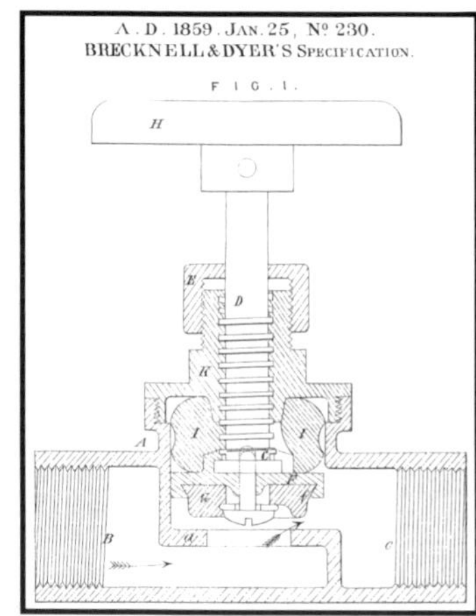

Photo 1.1 Henry Brecknell took out many patents in the 1850's and 1860's in connection with hydraulic components. It was patent work such as this which ensured the survival of his business in a fiercely competitive market. This is a patent for valves taken out in 1859, and the design formed the basis of all modern water taps.

Chapter 2 - Electric Traction Systems.

By the last quarter of the nineteenth century, the science of electricity was sufficiently developed for use as a traction system. The first electrified street tramway in England was at Blackpool, which started with a conduit system, with conductor rails buried in the road surface. Soon afterwards, in Leeds, overhead wires were being tried, and before long other towns and cities were promoting their own tramways with overhead wires. (The Blackpool system was converted to overhead wires in 1899.).

The detailed components involved in these overhead systems featured many brass and bronze castings, and Brecknell's company with its foundry practices met the requirement ideally. No doubt the Brecknell marketing eyes saw this as a growth opportunity. To boost the efforts, Edward Munro, an electrical engineer, joined company with Henry and Edwin Brecknell in 1892 and the name changed to Henry Brecknell, Sons and Munro, describing themselves as "Founders and Electrical Engineers". Munro brought with him knowledge of the electric traction business, and the combination of a brass foundry and the new technology of electricity gave a whole new market possibility as the world changed from hydraulic to electric power.

Following the example of Blackpool, several towns and cities were considering the possibility of updating their horse-drawn tramways. Some towns had already replaced their horses with steam tractors, but after the success in Leeds and Blackpool most schemes were advocating the use of electric trams with overhead lines. Brecknell's home city of Bristol was no exception, and plans were soon well advanced for conversion to electric traction. The great attraction of electricity was the absence of pollution in the streets - steam engines produced smoke, and horses their own waste, which became a considerable nuisance in the streets which were then only loose-dressed. Bristol, for example, in 1894 had 109 trams with 678 horses for the city centre routes. Brecknell's firm became involved in proposals for electrification, and in 1894 obtained the contract for a trial conversion of the line between Old Market and Kingswood. The scope of work was everything from the pavement surface to the trams, including poles, bracket arms, overhead wire and fittings, switchgear, trolley collectors and tram mountings. The excitement of that first contract must have been felt throughout the Brecknell company, but it came at the same time as the death of Edwin. He was aged only 36.

The Bristol trial line was an outstanding success, and the following year the first major contract was placed with Brecknell's for further electrification. More work followed, and by the turn of the century virtually all the Bristol lines were electrified using the Brecknell system. Contracts were obtained during the next few years for tramways in other towns in the south west, including Bath, Plymouth, Torquay, Exeter, and Taunton.

In July 1898 the team was strengthened by the arrival of Hugh Rogers, a foundry engineer. Further premises were acquired leasehold in September 1898 at 13-16 Henry Street. Yet further space was leased the following year in Jacob Street, and it is clear that an office in London was opened at this time. In 1904 the Company was reformed as Brecknell, Munro & Rogers, with the shares split between the three partners. Two years later, Henry retired due to ill health and his place was taken by his son, Henry E.F.Brecknell, grandson of the founder.

Early in 1909 Edward Munro left the Company, although remaining in charge of the London office until 1913. He was to become Chief Engineer of the Railless Electric Traction Co. Ltd. (RET) which was promoting and developing the science of trolleybuses, following pioneering work in Germany. There was still a strong connection, however, because from 1910 there was a formal agreement with RET for B,M&R to supply all the overhead line equipment and collectors for RET buses. The first British trolleybus system began in Leeds in June 1911, and there were a further nine systems in use within four years.

Overseas work was growing for the firm. Tramways were equipped in Boksburg and Shanghai in 1914, Bloemfontein in 1915 and the Toronto street tramway in 1921. These foreign contracts particularly needed experienced staff to supervise the installation work, and there were good opportunities for travel. One employee promoted to supervising work abroad was a young man named Arnold Willis, who had joined the Company in 1902 at the age of 16. He was made responsible for the contract in Brazil for 1922, and spent time in that country as work progressed.

Photo 2.1 This shows one of the first runs on the Bristol line, at a steeply graded street in St George, with a trailer in tow. The trolley collector has a simple tension spring for the contact force; this was later redesigned to place the spring inside the column and out of sight. The excitement of the first run of a new design, in a new environment, with many onlookers, has been repeated many times in the years since this picture was taken. (Peter Davey Collection).

Photo 2.2 The attractive Brecknell poles and bracket arms are evident in this view of a tram climbing to College Green, Bristol, from the Tramways Centre, taken around 1905. (Peter Davey Collection).

Photo 2.3 Edward Munro (Courtesy Gabriel Summers, his great grand-daughter).

Photo 2.4 Brecknell, Munro and Rogers received a large order for an overhead system in Petrograd, USSR (later Leningrad) and the installation was personally supervised by Edward Munro in 1904. The photograph shows installation proceeding in Nevsky Prospect with the existing horse-drawn trams still running. The tram system remains in St.Petersburg today, with much of the original equipment still in place. (Courtesy Michael Brown, Alpha and Omega).

Photos 2.5 and 2.6 Two views of a line insulator of the 1910 era. The outer casing is of cast iron, with a composition insulation within. Many thousands of these units were made by B,M&R and many continue in service today.

Photo 2.7 Brecknell devised an ingenious device to avoid the tram driver walking the pole around at the terminus, and this example of the 'Automatic Reverser' is shown in Bristol. The tram only has to set back slowly, whereupon the trolley head is encouraged around a reversing triangle by the use of three spring-back frogs. (courtesy W.A.Camwell)

Chapter 3 - New Products and Acquisitions

With the coming of war in 1914 the main production lines of the Company were turned over to munitions. B,M&R contributed greatly to the west country war effort and actually increased its staff - by the end of 1918 there were more than a thousand people employed. The aftermath of the war was difficult, however. Copies of catalogues of the period show rapid rises in prices and of course the whole export business, with the network of agents, had been distorted or destroyed during the war.

B,M&R began to look to diversifying its operations. Because of the extensive mechanical expertise which had been gained, it was decided to move into automatic machinery, and the Company signed a contract with the American Machinery and Foundry Company to manufacture under licence that company's "Standard" cigarette-making machine. This equipment was sold in quantity to the Imperial and British American Tobacco Companies, and the manufacturing operation brought a gradual increase in awareness of smaller mechanical assemblies. In 1919, the Company took over the Tobacco and Machinery division of Cosmos Engineering, resulting in a major share of the cigarette-making machinery business. At the same time the Peckham Truck and Engineering Company become the sole UK sales agency for B,M&R traction products.

In addition, B,M&R were associated with companies making gears and bicycles, and developed machinery for making corrugated paper. There were also some most unusual associated design contracts, such as petrol pumps, a variety of ticket dispensing machines, and even a feather-plucking machine. The traction side was busy developing new products, including sanding gear for trams, signal lamps and indicators, and grinding attachments to remove corrugations from running rails. The vast increase in product range brought with it an increase in turnover. Henry E.F.Brecknell was the prime mover in this diversification activity, demonstrating mechanical ingenuity with business acumen, while Arnold Willis, after a series of promotions, now led the sales force.

Production was now condensed into just two sites - the general engineering division was in Thrissell Street, Bristol, and the electrical and foundry divisions in Pennywell Road, together with a small development team under Harry Dolman, working on a prototype automatic ticket machine for London Transport. The trade in cigarette machinery, however, was growing and the big tobacco companies were looking on. In 1920 Imperial Tobacco and British American Tobacco announced a joint majority holding in B,M&R, to gain control of this important technology. Meanwhile, Molins, a family business of Cuban origin, had manufactured a new type of machine and this company became a notable competitor to B,M&R.

All this diversification was happening at a time of turmoil in the tramways business. Many of the early electric tramways, including several of the early B,M&R systems, had been forced to close after only twenty or thirty years because of disputes with the local authority about electricity supplies and the maintenance of the road surface beside and between the tracks. Trolleybuses avoided the road arguments and were seen as a method of extending the life of electric urban transport while in many cases making use of the same basic overhead systems adapted, of course, by provision of a second contact wire. B,M&R was led enthusiastically into this market by Arnold Willis, who with his international contacts, had built up some reputation in the field, and Edward Munro at RET continued to offer consultancy advice. They were supported by the development team, which produced several types of trolley collector which would provide essential products as the Company cornered the bus supply market. A major conference in Bournemouth in July 1922 saw Edward Munro present a paper describing these developments and extolling the virtues of the new collector technology.

Meanwhile, the team began to look towards the mainline railways for business. An improved version of the industrial diamond style pantograph was produced, and early in 1924 this was supplied to the LMS Railway for trials on the Lancaster, Morecambe and Heysham line. The contact force was achieved from springs working through levers, but the LMS were not happy with the variations in head contact force this produced. The B,M&R Engineering Manager, M.D.Gilroy-Stuart changed the design to include a chain around a cam profile, giving in effect a variable leverage; in this way it was possible to maintain an even contact force throughout the working range. This prototype was found a great success on the LMS railway, and substantial orders followed. (It is interesting to note that the use of a chain around a cam was a feature of the modern pantograph patent of 1973).

By the late nineteen twenties the traction business had reached a plateau. Over 60 towns in Britain were running their tramways with Brecknell equipment - places as diverse as Llanelli, Grimsby and Stoke on Trent. This was, however, a period of rising labour costs, particularly in the London Area, and London County Council were having difficulty keeping their trams clean. B,M&R designed and supplied two prototype washing plants on a trial basis. The next year one machine was purchased for £600 for permanent installation at the Holloway Depot, and a tender for 30 machines to equip all London tram depots was won by B,M&R, and all were installed by March 1928. This caused a political upset within the LCC because 320 car washing employees were made redundant. The tramway authority, under heavy omnibus competition, had no alternative method of saving money, although these men were re-employed in the road maintenance department. For Brecknell's, these contracts for tram washing represented a major diversification of design as the electric traction business reached a plateau of demand.

The pantographs on the LMS railway had not gone unnoticed, and early in 1927 B,M&R obtained a contract through British Thomson Houston for the supply of similar units for the Bombay, Baroda, and Central Indian Railway which took 18 months to complete. Similar design units were supplied to the Swansea and Mumbles railway in 1927, and to the Blackpool tramway in 1928. This work was so successful that a strong relationship was formed with BTH which, with its successors AEI, GEC, and Alstom has continued to the present day.

Changes in the cigarette business were to threaten the Company in 1927. Molins were taken over by British Tobacco, and in effect were in control of B,M&R. With the management emphasis very much on the machinery side, the traction interests were rather left out on a limb, the situation being reinforced in early 1928 when the Traction and Foundry division moved to 114 Jacob Street, a site which had been purchased two years previously. The two sides of the business continued to grow separately.

Photo 3.1 The Bristol factory contained many small buildings; this view shows the forge and drop hammer.

Photo 3.2 A selection of B,M&R collectors has been set out on display at the Bristol factory. In the foreground can be seen various wheel collectors, including in the centre foreground a four wheel collector similar to that in photo 3.4. To the rear are various trolley and bow collectors.

Photo 3.3 Hugh Rogers, Charlie Merritt, Henry E.F.Brecknell and Arnold Willis are pictured at the 1925 Christmas Dinner and Dance.

Photo 3.4 One of the earliest surviving B,M&R official photographs shows a simple tow trolley system fitted to a mining locomotive. The design would be perfectly at home in a modern cartoon book! Note particularly the hanging bob weight for stability and the trailing cable which appears to foul the adjacent track. The signals in the background are of Great Northern Railway somersault pattern but the precise date and location of the photograph are unknown. These tow trolley systems were sold widely for contractor operations, and feature in the contemporary catalogue.

Photo 3.5 This 1920's shoegear was probably designed for industrial use, rather than railway, judging by the width of the shoe. The mechanism is similar, however, to systems in use on the Southern Railway at the time.

Photo 3.6 Although B,M&R had made pantographs for many years, there had been no sales to mainline railways. All that changed, however, in 1924 when a trial unit was supplied to the Lancaster, Morecambe, and Heysham railway (part of the LMS). The contact force was by springs actuated by a large vacuum cylinder, working from the train vacuum brake system.

Photo 3.7 Slip rings formed a large part of the business in the 1920's, in use at steel works, large industrial sites and dockyards where traction currents required to be transferred to a rotating shaft.

Photos 3.8 and 3.9 The pantograph for the Bombay, Baroda and Central Indian Railway 1926, with inset showing the details of the pan head secondary suspension using torsion springs. Such suspension was a real innovation at the time, when pantographs were considered as relatively crude pieces of equipment, suitable only for low speeds.

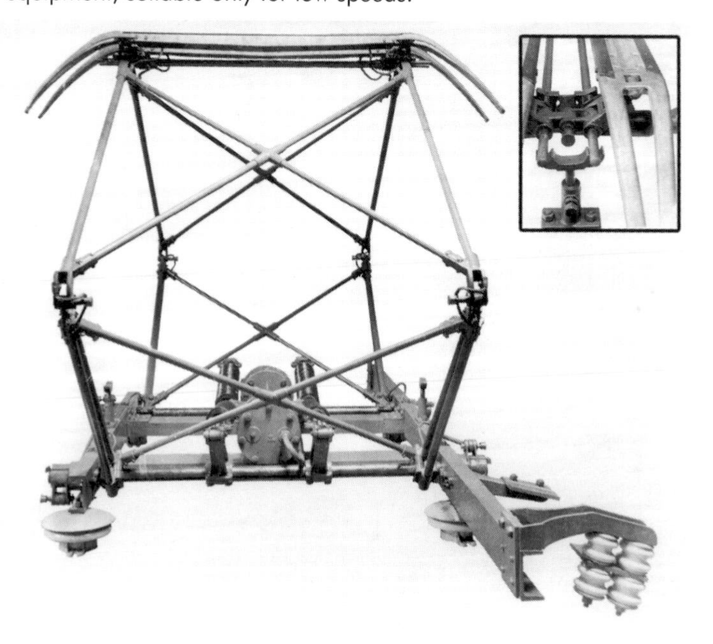

Photo 3.10 Three phase power supplies in industry required three-pole collectors - this is a design from 1925 for a small electric stores vehicle.

Photo 3.11 A selection of B,M&R products from the 1920's has been laid out in the factory. At this time a wide range of aluminium overhead fittings were made, and some may be seen to the rear of the bench. Notice the large selection of roller collectors; neutral sections to the right, and the period costumes hanging in the background!

Chapter 4 - The Move to Chard.

The traction business had a separate market to the rest of the Company, and needed to be treated differently. It was only a matter of time before the division would be sold off, and in June 1928 B,M&R agreed terms with Arnold Willis for a management buyout. Willis therefore bought the Traction and Foundry Division at Jacob Street such that he would set up a limited company in due course. Separately, the remaining organisation at the Pennywell Road factory went through a similar process, and in November 1928 a new company, Brecknell, Munro & Rogers, (1928) Ltd. was incorporated. The Chairman was Henry E.F.Brecknell.

So the company split - the machinery side under Henry E.F.Brecknell continued as Brecknell, Munro and Rogers(1928), and the former traction division became Brecknell, Willis and Company.

While the subsequent story of B,M&R does not form part of this book, it is worth recording a few points. Manufacturing of cigarette making machinery ceased and the company concentrated on making machinery for the manufacture and printing of corrugated paper. Henry E.F.Brecknell was to continue with B,M&R before setting up business alone in Keynsham in 1929. He died in 1933. The Development Manager, Harry Dolman, became a partner and the Company was renamed Brecknell, Dolman and Rogers, and continued trading under that name for many years. Harry Dolman was later to become well known as chairman of Bristol City Football Club. B,D&R later became Giffard Engineering, and there are offshoots still trading in the Bristol area.

Brecknell, Willis & Co. Ltd. was formally incorporated on 13th February 1929. On the development side, the new organisation was free from the restraining influences of the machinery business, and could settle down to some proper product development. The gradual abandonment of the old style trams and replacement with trolleybuses was accompanied by a change in expectations in society. In earlier years passengers expected to travel on the top deck ('outside') open to the elements, but the new generations of trolleybus riders expected more, and the new designs had enclosed upper decks with a proper roof. This gave a problem where bus routes passed under low railway bridges in town centres, for the higher vehicle left very little room for the trolley collector and overhead wires in the space between the roof and the bridge. With an eye on this growing trolleybus market, various collector designs from the 1920's were developed and refined to produce a new, low-profile and lightweight collector. It was not the first time that the business development had followed social change, but it was a spectacular success. The 1930 design was championed by Gilroy-Stuart and Arnold Willis and trialled at Wolverhampton, then 150 units were sold to London in 1932 and 1933 and sales blossomed. The design was subsequently improved over the years by the incorporation of snubbers, swing restrictors, and hydraulic dampers, to cope with increased speeds and to minimise dewirements.

The latter part of the 1920's saw a number of schemes aimed at boosting employment and upgrading the country's infrastructure. One such scheme was for wholesale electrification of the main railways in England, and this culminated in a detailed report from the Ministry of Transport in 1928. This laid down plans which, had they come to fruition, would have resulted in large areas of the country being electrified using overhead wires, and would have given a much-needed boost to the business. Unfortunately, the plan was shelved, and BW was forced to work harder to obtain work from overseas. Worse still, a Royal Commission on Transport in 1931 was convened to study the public transport in the major cities. Its report included the damning statement:

"Tramways, if not an obsolete form of transport, are at all events in a state of obsolescence and cause much unnecessary congestion. ....We recommend therefore that... they should gradually disappear and give place to other forms of transport".

This report did more than anything else to change the attitudes of local corporation transport organisations away from the urban tramway. As attitudes changed, the tramways closed or were converted into trolleybus lines, and the market for tramway overhead diminished rapidly. In May 1931 redundancies were announced among senior staff at BW, including M.D.Gilroy-Stuart. Short of money, BW also raised a mortgage of £2000 in 1933 against its land and premises in Jacob Street. The difficulties were to continue throughout the thirties.

With the prospect of war, the British government was providing financial assistance for the relocation of engineering companies away from large cities vulnerable to bombing, and Brecknell's began to look for a country site. The choice was Chard, a small town on the south western edge of Somerset, which had some reputation for industry in what was mainly rural surroundings. Here, on land off East Street was the Station Road Iron Works, the home of A.L.Hockey's lace making machinery business, and BW bought the site and buildings in April 1938. Further from East Street was the site of Denings factory, known as Somerset Works, and both sites were accessed by the narrow Tapstone Lane, which passed down the middle, between buildings.

Immediately a refurbishment programme began. The foundry was moved from Bristol in October of that year. With war threatening, the remaining manufacturing operation was moved to Chard during 1939 leaving only sales, accounts, and administration at the registered office at Jacob Street. It was a timely move, because the Bristol site was severely damaged by bombing in January 1941, fortunately without casualties. The bombs did, however, destroy all the sales records and the collection of glass plate photographs. (Although the Company survived, the bombing caused the cessation of trams in Bristol, for a subsequent air raid produced a direct hit on the main tramway power station. With no electricity, the tram service ceased, never to restart).

In the Drawing Office in 1943 there was a good sort out of the Company's pre-war designs. Most of those considered as suitable for future work were traced onto new paper with the BW title being made with a rubber stamp. The work started slowly as war pressures allowed, and was still going on in 1950. Most early drawings which drawings survive in the archives are from this period.

Once again, the manufacturing side of the operation was turned over to the war effort. May Willis, wife of Arnold, was appointed Personnel Director with specific responsibility for the welfare of the large number of female workers employed on munitions manufacture. She and her husband lived at Templecloud, near Bristol, but during the week lodged in rented rooms at the house beside the site at Chard, known as 'The Elms'. The house, which dated from 1900 occupied a fine position overlooking the site, and was still owned by the Hockey family, along with the adjacent two fields.

Soon after the move to Somerset, it was obvious that more room was needed for the factory. In July 1944, land between Tapstone Lane and the old Chard Town railway station was purchased, along with Somerset Works and Old Town Mill. For the moment, Somerset Works remained leased to Denings who had right of access along Tapstone Lane. The purchase also included ownership of the private siding off the railway, previously used by Hockey to despatch output from his factory, and for the first time, BW had a direct frontage onto East Street. The total area of land owned by BW amounted to 20½ acres and would give much more flexibility as things developed. Meanwhile, the Jacob Street site in Bristol was sold in 1945.

The end of the war in Europe in May 1945 was a cause for celebration, and a large party was held. Arnold Willis thanked his employees and explained that as a result of their efforts in ensuring the continuing profitability of his Company, and his own consultancy work, he had become a millionaire! The immediate post-war period saw a similar period of uncertainly as in 1918. Export work, particularly, on which the Company had thrived, was difficult to obtain. In the face of these challenges, discussions took place between BW and the Anti-Attrition Metal Company, of Maidenhead, as to a possible sale of BW. A-A had existed for many years as a competitor to BW for collectors, although there was some inter-trading. After much wrangling, BW was bought by A-A in April 1947, but the BW trading name was continued, and Arnold Willis remained in charge. There was a rapid change in systems in the Company, and within weeks of the change all drawings from the BW design office were appearing on Anti-Attrition drawing sheets.

Arnold Willis had suffered from heart trouble, and in May 1950 he underwent an operation from which he did not recover. He was 63. BW had lost a well-loved leader and was left in a poor position to take on the changes which were to follow.

Photo 4.1. As well as conventional trolley collectors, Brecknell, Willis manufactured several types of bow collectors for tramways. This picture shows a BW bow on the roof of a tramcar in London in 1928.

Photo 4.2 The Brecknell, Munro and Rogers Thrissell Street machine shop was a dramatic place in 1928, with all machines driven by flat belt line shafting. In the foreground are large pulleywheel castings. The site at Thrissell Street, Bristol, remained with Brecknell Munro and Rogers when the split came, with Brecknell, Willis retaining the Jacob Street factory.

Photo 4.3 The Westhoe colliery railway in Gateshead was electrified in the 1920's using pantographs and overhead system supplied by B,M&R. The line is disused today, and electric traction ceased in 1989. The use of positive and negative wires with twin pantographs was a most unusual innovation, and not taken up generally.

Photo 4.4 Brecknell, Willis trolleybus collector dated 1930. Many thousands of these units were supplied, and similar units are still in use today. The contact force was provided by the two tension springs mounted alongside the central pole.

Photo 4.5 London 'Diddler' Trolleybus featuring the new BW collectors in 1934.
(courtesy Bryan Woodriff – London Transport Museum)

Photo 4.6 Many trams were still using roller collectors, like this unit, dating from 1930.

Photo 4.7 Junctions on trolleybus systems resulted in exceedingly complicated overhead assemblies. This view shows a double line trolleybus crossover in Ipswich in the 1930's, and visible are several neutral sections to isolate the different power supply sections. The insulation here is by Permali material, a beech laminate-reinforced phenolic.

Photo 4.8 The BW line marker, for the painting of lines on tennis courts and cricket pitches. There were at least two different sizes manufactured.

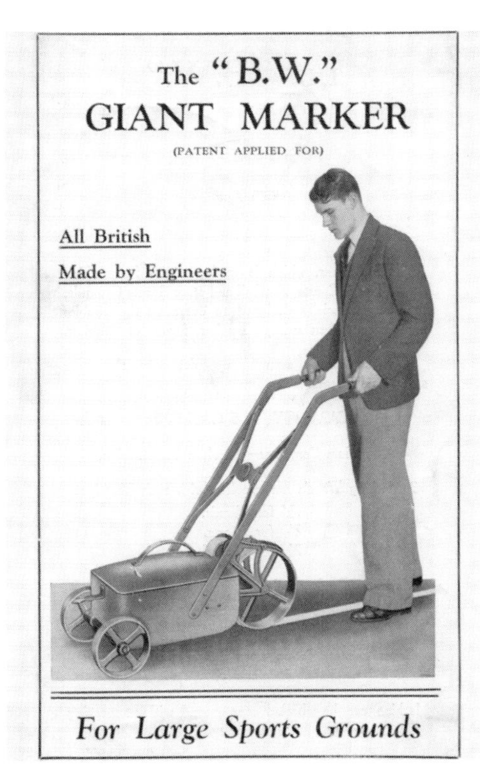

Photo 4.9 The first Brecknell, Willis football team 1936 - 1937.

Photo 4.10 In 1938 the company moved to the town of Chard to avoid potential war damage. This picture is the official opening ceremony of the Chard factory, where the staff had the chance to view not only the new site, but Chard and its surroundings. For many of the group the move from Bristol must have been a major upheaval in their lives.

Photo 4.11 View of Chard works in 1938, taken from alongside the road opposite the Victoria Public House. In the foreground is the area of land once a farm. Just out of the picture to the left is the Chard Town station, closed to passengers in 1916 but still in use for goods traffic until the 1960's. On the right is the gatehouse; centre is the factory manager's house; and beyond are the main machine shop and foundry. The gatehouse survives, along with the building on the far left, now the Engineering unit. To the extreme left are the same trees which now line the road up to 'The Elms', with the chimneys of 'The Elms' itself just visible in the background. The roadway between the fence in the foreground and the buildings is the original Tapstone Lane. When the Company expanded, this lane became an internal company road, and a new Tapstone Road was built in the immediate foreground of the picture.

Photo 4.12 Another view of the site in 1938, looking towards the factory manager's house. The Victoria public house is in the far background. The building on the left survives as part of the machine shop and commercial offices above. Note the Company motor cars of the period! The main buildings on the right, which housed the machine shops, were demolished in the 1960's and the site then formed a quadrangle of steelwork and equipment store until the landscaping work associated with the centenary in 1994.

Photo 4.13 Just before the war, the Company had plans for a grand new entrance building. A model was commissioned, and the view here shows it with the distinctive 1930's style architecture. Had the project proceeded, it would undoubtedly have been a fine addition to the Chard landscape - in the event, the project was postponed due to the war and never taken up.

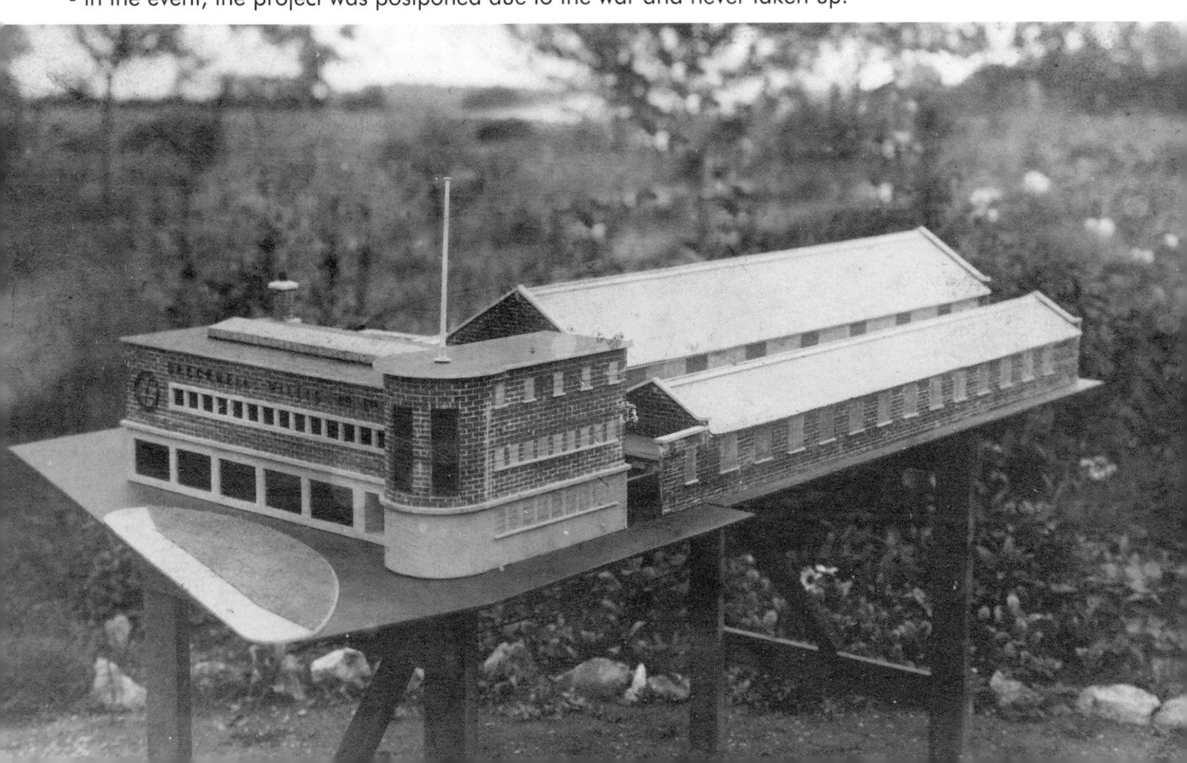

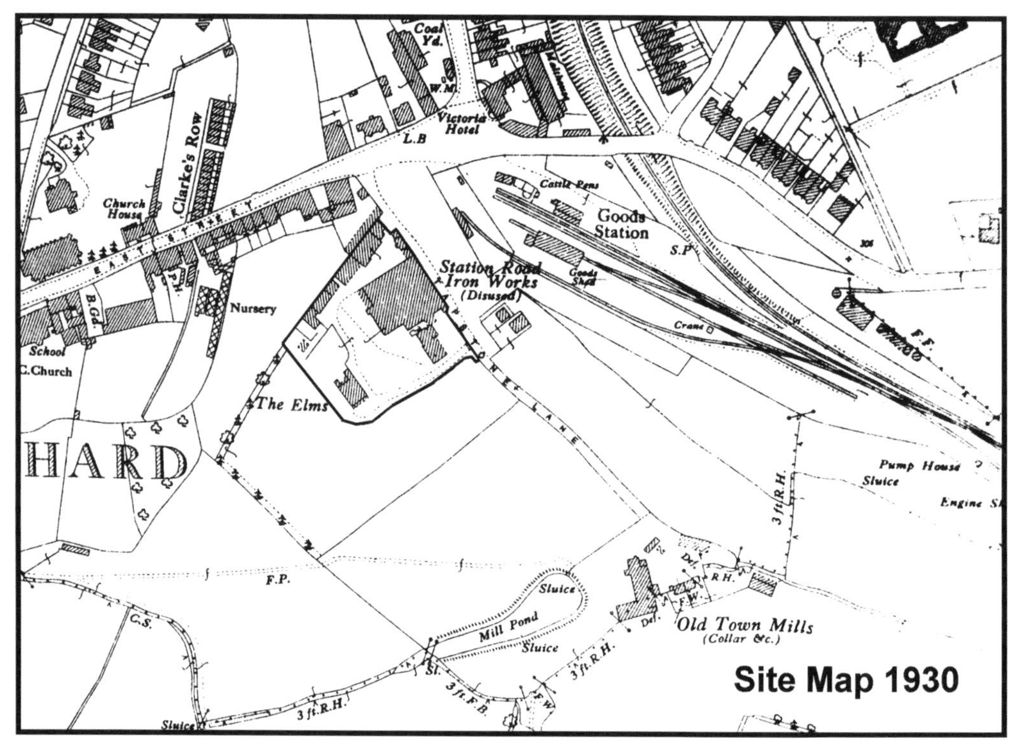

Photo 4.14 Map of Chard in 1930, showing the disused Station Road Iron Works. The area purchased by BW in 1937 has been outlined. Notice the private siding off the railway, and the narrow route of Tapstone Lane passing the factory gate.

Photo 4.15 A sawbench straight from the BW production line in 1939.

Photo 4.16 A group of the sales staff outside the Jacob Street Office in 1939. It was this building which was bombed two years later.

Photo 4.17 Munitions from the second world war, produced at Chard.

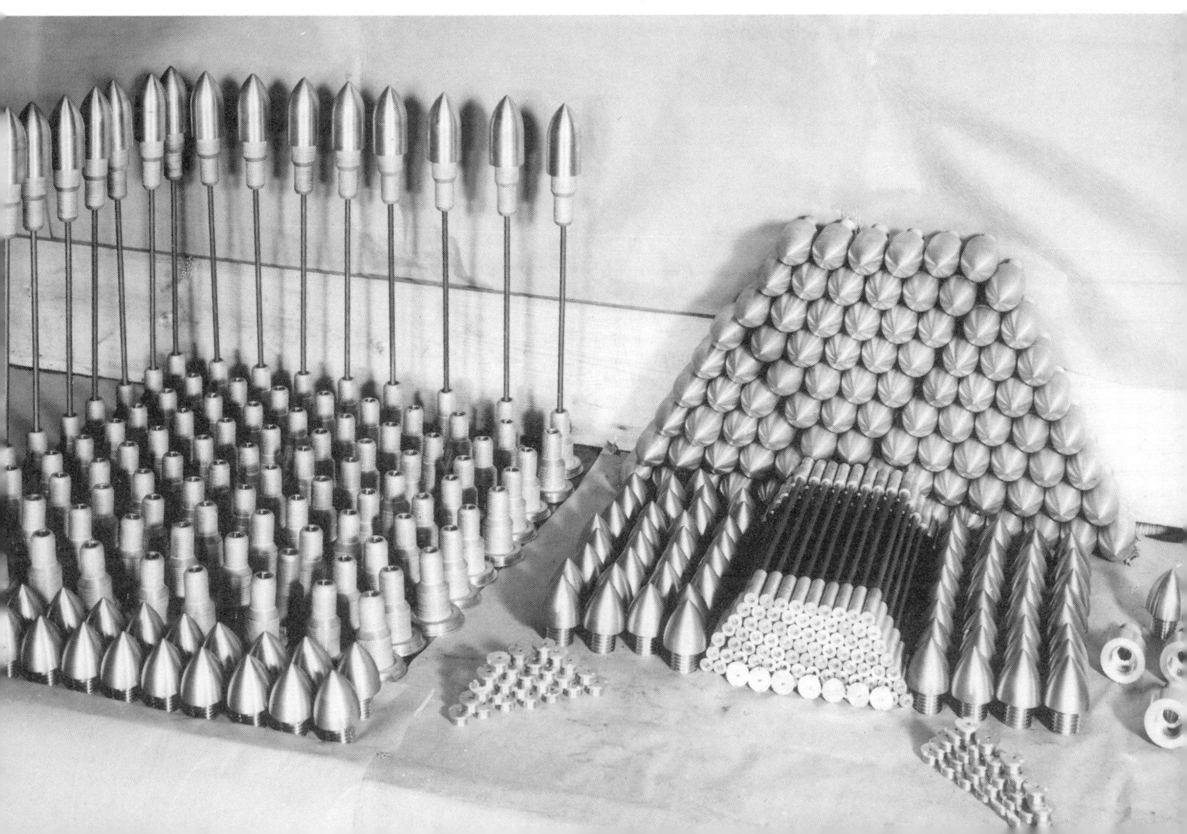

Chapter 5 - Collapse of the Business.

The immediate post-war period was difficult for the country and for industry. Rationing of fuel remained in force for several years, bringing extra pressure on public transport systems already strained by the lack of maintenance during the hostilities. Gradually, however, refurbishment and repair work increased, bringing new orders for Brecknell, Willis, and the improvements brought by the new owners, Anti-Attrition, began to bear fruit.

With the setback in business after the war, the extra land bought in 1944 had not been utilised. The area beside the railway was undeveloped, and the Denings factory remained leased out. Meanwhile, the opportunity arose to buy 'The Elms' and the two adjacent fields. It seemed logical to use the sale of one to finance the other. First off was the sale of the Denings site to their parent organisation Beyer, Peacock and Company, the locomotive builders, for £1300, sold in April 1952. A year later, BW purchased 'The Elms', from the Hockey family, along with the adjoining two fields, and as if to put a stamp on the proceedings, the following spring the BW registered office finally moved from Bristol to Station Works, Chard. The move from Bristol was complete.

During the site adjustments, there was some correspondence with British Railways over the private siding. In a letter from them dated 1952, BW was asked what its intentions were about moving goods by rail. BR noted that the siding had been in use since 1905, and although no traffic had been sent since 1949, the annual rent of £1 5s 4d was still payable, with three years' worth of payments outstanding. Subsequent letters threatened the disconnection of the siding. Evidently, the directors of BW were not to be harassed in this way and the siding was disconnected within a few years, with no record of any BW goods being shipped by rail.

An interesting enquiry was received from the Gloucester Railway Carriage and Wagon Company in 1952. They had secured a contract for building the trains for the new Toronto underground system, and required shoegear. BW designed and built the first units and there were follow-on orders in subsequent years.

In February 1958 Anti-Attrition were themselves bought by Beyer, Peacock, and with them, of course, Brecknell, Willis. Steam locomotive production at Beyer, Peacock was virtually at an end, and they were desperate to diversify by acquiring other companies and technologies.

Early in 1961, BW recorded the sale of the 10,000th set of trolleybus collector equipment to the 1930 design. This had been well proven in service, and was being manufactured under licence in other countries. (Examples were seen in the late 1970's in the USSR and Italy, and were still in service in Athens in 2000). More covered accommodation was needed, and in 1962 a new building was erected on the edge of land adjoining the Chard Town goods station, intended as an assembly shop for longer items of machinery. The valuable land at Chard was attracting the local council's eyes. A by-pass was projected to carry industrial traffic between the proposed industrial estates of Tapstone Road and Millfield, the route to run through the middle of the site, and past the front door of 'The Elms'. This was fortunately not pursued, for it would have split the site in half.

With the continuing fall in traction business, new products were sought. Wilfred Liddington joined BW as a director in 1962 and brought with him his own patent design for a tool and cutter grinding machine. After much trouble, only one prototype was completed, and this was scrapped a few years later.

The work available in both the foundry and the general engineering divisions of BW was decreasing. In January 1963, the dreadful winter weather coincided with half the staff being made redundant from both the main factory and the engineering division. By May 1963 the foundry output was down to only 5 tons weekly, and in June a further 40 redundancies were declared.

With the growing use of the private car and the development of diesel buses, the number of trolleybus systems in Britain declined. By 1966 there were only a small number in service, and the market for overhead parts was much reduced. BICC had been a competitor to BW for overhead work, but now offered all its trolleybus overhead designs for sale. The management at BW saw this as a good opportunity to regain control of the market, such as it was, and agreed to purchase the entire collection of drawings, patterns, and castings. (It was to take six years, however, before the deal was concluded, by which time all remaining trolleybuses in Britain had been scrapped. It was all rather ironic, since many of these components had been copied from B,M&R designs in the twenties).

In the face of such a depressing outlook for the business, it seems strange that in 1966 a new workshop building was planned and erected on the east side of Tapstone Lane, and on the site of the former private siding. This was a steel-framed structure fitted with a new design of roof support pioneered by Denings, and was to be one of the largest buildings in Chard. The structure was assembled and brought into use during the year as the main assembly hall for BW, and was a vast improvement on any of the existing site buildings. By now, Denings and BW were both owned by Beyer, Peacock, and there was much overlap between the two companies. Both sets of employees were eligible for the BP pension scheme, and a joint Sports and Social Club was formed. The two foundries were merged, and the site opened up by the removal of fences, to appear to the uninitiated as if it were one operation. Denings changed their name to Space Decks in January 1967, as their business began to concentrate on bespoke roofing designs.

Business was not good, however, for either company. The joint foundry ceased production and closed in August 1968. Without a foundry, BW was at a severe disadvantage, and its own activities reduced further. It was only a matter of time before action would be taken, and on 16th October 1968 the dreaded notice arrived - Beyer, Peacock announced the closure of Brecknell, Willis. All business activity would cease on completion of the current order book, and assets would be transferred within BP or sold. Brecknell, Willis would cease to exist. Over the next few months trade decayed, and the directors resigned one by one. The number of staff employed dropped to twenty, and activity reduced to solely packing and dispatching products from the stores. The new assembly hall was vacated, and after a while in Space Decks hands, was rented by Norringtons, the tractor company, as their workshop and showroom. By early 1969 BW was virtually closed.

At Beyer, Peacock itself, a new director was appointed, Robert Kirkaldie. One of his tasks was to organise the winding up of the Chard operations, and sell off the assets. After a few months, however, it was clear that BW was still surviving, and he instead developed an interest in keeping it going. A new enthusiasm grew within the staff to survive, and the dismal trading position reached a low point, and began to climb. The closure was postponed.

Kirkaldie believed in the company, and he lobbied Beyer, Peacock to persevere. There is no doubt that but for his efforts, BW would have gone the way of most of the other BP subsidiaries, and closed. Instead, as we shall see, BW was able to rebuild itself and regain its worldwide reputation against all the odds.

The "B.W." DRUM TROLLEY

LIFTS,

TILTS

and CARRIES

SAVES LABOUR

PROTECTS YOUR EMPLOYEES

Keeps Your Works and Roads Tidy

Photo 5.1 BW made a number of useful tooling aids in the 1940's. This picture shows a publicity leaflet for a drum carrier.

Photo 5.2 The BW Cricket Team won the local cup in 1949. In the back row is Hardy Stoodley, (who appears again in photo 7.15). (courtesy David Wheadon).

Photo 5.3 The Company ran a coach trip to London in 1949 - here is the excited group before setting off from Chard. (Courtesy David Wheadon).

Photo 5.4 To celebrate the coronation of Queen Elizabeth II in 1953 a number of special commemorative bronze teapot stands were produced in the Company foundry.

Photo 5.5 Brecknell, Willis staff in 1953. Informal group photograph taken outside the 1962 building, now the paint shop.

Photo 5.6 Inside the machine shop in 1957. The lathe has been decorated as celebration of the employee leaving to join the RAF. (courtesy the late Peter Stevens).

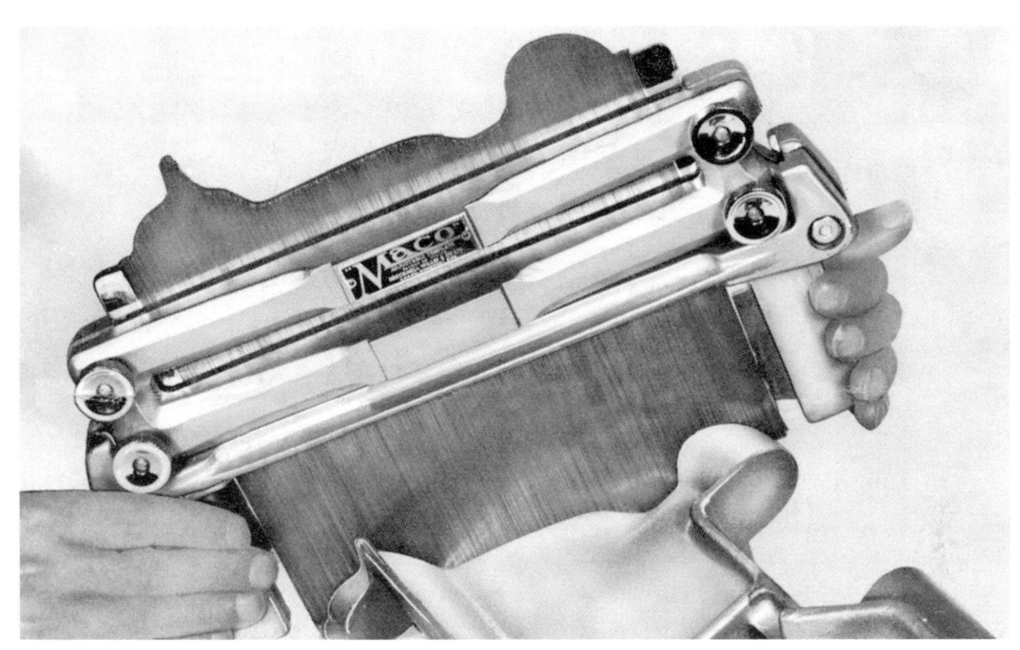

Photo 5.7 The MACO template was a device for transferring the outline of a moulding or pattern onto a drawing or other form. Brecknell, Willis made many hundreds of these devices in three sizes.

Photo 5.8 This is the building put up in 1961 next to the Chard Town Goods yard. In this photograph the building is just one year old. In the left foreground are trolleybus collectors, on the right a batch of Toronto collectors, are being assembled, and to the left is the base frame of the cutter grinder prototype. (courtesy Chris Beer).

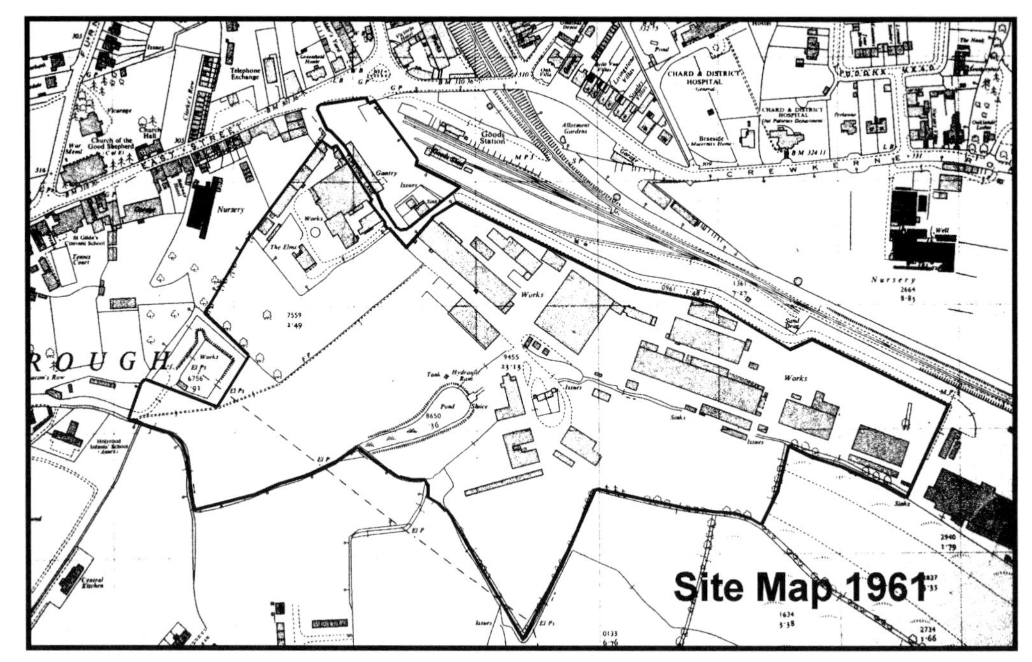

Photo 5.8-B Map of the Chard site in 1961, showing the site boundary in heavy line. The 20-acre area includes several fields to the south, the former Old Town Mill, and also the plot adjacent to the railway, which is the other side of Tapstone Lane. Past the entrance drive to 'The Elms' a new road has been constructed to bypass the rest of the site and give access to further factories to the south east. Note that the private siding has been truncated at the site boundary.

Photo 5.9 In 1962 BW built a number of machines for the manufacture of toilet rolls. The photograph shows a small section of what was a 150ft long production line during proving trials. (courtesy David Wheadon).

Photo 5.10 The design for the magnetic petrol cap dated from Brecknell, Munro and Rogers days, but examples were still being made in the 1960's. They were used on vehicles as diverse as London Buses and Aston Martin motor cars.

Photo 5.11 The last section of the roof is erected on the new BW assembly hall in October 1966. On the extreme left is the entrance to the old station, and between the hut and the new building is the trackbase of the old BW private siding. (Photo courtesy David Wheadon).

Photo 5.12 A Ford Escort body shell emerges from the paint tank at Halewood. BW supplied the collector gear which ensured an electric charge on the body shell to encourage the deposit of paint into all areas and crevices to effectively prevent rusting. This was the start of a number of subsequent dip-tank electrification projects over the next few years.

Chapter 6 - A New Pantograph

Kirkaldie's optimistic ideas for Company development needed technical support, and a new structure was created in January 1971, and included a small design team. The ideas needed promotion, and he appointed a new marketing manager, Kenneth McQueen. Ken had worked for Associated Electrical Industries (formerly British Thompson Houston) and had a large knowledge of railway traction work. This was to turn out as one of the most important appointments in the Company's history, for Ken was to lead the rebirth of the organisation as a railway and tramway traction business. His first task was to promote the development of a new style pantograph.

In April 1973 Patent No. 1506855 was granted to Brecknell Willis for an "Electric Current Collecting Pantograph". This was a single arm design, with the unique feature of having all the control linkages encased within the arms. It was a big improvement on the old B,M&R diamond design, and was derived from the conceptual designs of a GEC consultant engineer, Bob Whiteley. It was conceived principally for light rail or rapid transit applications. At the centre of the design was the elbow assembly, featuring a cam and chains, very similar to the concept of the Bombay pantograph fifty years earlier. Three prototype pantographs were built, for which trials in widely differing locations had been arranged. The first was a local tramway at Seaton, Devon, which was a narrow-gauge tourist line with speeds up to 25 mph. The second was on the Blackpool Tramway, replacing the trolley pole collector; and the third was on the MBTA "Blueline" in Boston, USA, a commuter line where speeds up to 60 mph were reached. Early in 1974 a fourth prototype was accepted by British Rail for trials on its Eastern Region electrified lines.

Space Decks and BW activities remained closely aligned. The land assets handed to Space Decks in 1968 were formally transferred back to BW, and there were several staff movements between the organisations. One transfer in October 1974 was a young engineer named Tony White, appointed to work on the new pantograph development.

With all the focus on the new pantograph work, it was easy to forget that it was the sales to British heavy industry which were keeping BW going. A new product, Brecktrack, was introduced to provide an insulated replacement for bare wire overhead systems, and sales were encouraging, but overall the Company remained in difficulties. It was clear that the new developments were causing the team to over-reach itself. There was little choice but to restructure, and in November 1975 two managers, and all part-time staff in accounts and engineering were made redundant. It was a setback, but hopefully the seeds of success had been sown already. The marketplace would decide.

By February 1976, the four prototype pantographs had completed 10,000 miles in trial operation. As a result a further four units were being delivered to British Rail, two further units to MBTA and Blackpool, two units to the Illinois Central Railway, one unit to Vicrail Australia, and two units to South Africa for general trials in mining and railway situations. Two units were also already in use on prototype vehicles at the Tyne and Wear Metro test track at Newcastle. Clearly the wide variety of these applications, and the differing climatic conditions experienced, indicated a favourable response by users to the new BW design. That summer was the hottest since records began. Temperatures of over 100degF were recorded in the factory area, and for much of the summer the daily hours of work were changed to 6.00 am - 2.30 pm.

The Newcastle Tyne and Wear Metro was the first of the new generation tram-like light rail schemes in Britain. The two BW prototype pantographs on the test track had worked well, and the great day came on 4th October 1976 when BW received the order for the complete build of 100 pantographs from GEC Traction - the first volume order for the new design.

Meanwhile, on British Rail the prototypes had not run quite so well. Incidents with the overhead line were put down to the lightweight nature of the design compared with the traditional pantographs running, and there was some opposition as a result. The research division, however, had taken an interest, and felt that the BW design could provide the basis of a new generation high speed pantograph as a means of increasing line speeds on the existing BR overhead wire. After some negotiation, in November 1976 the BR research department and Brecknell, Willis signed a technical collaboration agreement which allowed for joint technical work, and commercial benefit to both parties in the event of successful sales to other railways. At the time the agreement was unusual, and it remained one of only a few public/private sector agreements within the British Rail era. (Indeed, it was still being cited as a triumph in the 1990s when the privatisation of BR was well in-hand). A prototype unit was tested in the laboratory before starting trial service on the west coast route.

During May 1977, Ken McQueen, now Managing Director, joined a British overseas trade mission to Australasia and the Far East. This marketing tour covered 11 centres, and over 40,000 miles. A major result was the appointment of BW agents in five countries, together with several new orders. Prospects in the areas were seen as good, and a sound basis was established for BW's expansion in the future. That autumn, Mr. M.D.Gilroy-Stuart visited the Company as a guest. Although in his late seventies, he was delighted to be on Brecknell, Willis territory once again. He shared with the staff his reminiscences of B,M&R in the twenties, and contributed much information on the history which would otherwise have been lost. Meanwhile, Robert Kirkaldie retired from BW having served 8 years as a director, and after seeing BW climb back from the abyss.

In North America the reaction to the new pantograph design had been most enthusiastic and a production batch was ordered for use on the MBTA Blue Line, Boston. To aid business, and allow local manufacture, in January 1978 an agreement was signed with Ringsdorff Corporation for manufacture and sale of BW products in north America. Also in January 1978 the new BW pension scheme was set up, with trustees appointed, and included one shop-floor employee, Nigel Heselton.

During 1978 there was some development on a range of battery electric trucks. Several prototypes were produced, and these were offered as trial vehicles, aimed at the small industrial market. In another step forward, orders were received from Thorne Electronics Ltd. for the manufacture and installation of conveyor belt systems at their Ferguson Television Factory during 1978/79. A special area was set up in the old Denings building for the assembly. To create more office space, 'The Elms', which had been empty since 1976 was refurbished at a cost of £3000, and reoccupied by the new BW for sales, accounts and senior staff. The house still retained many of its original features, including an elegant staircase, fireplaces in all rooms, and a spectacular tiled hallway. These were all carefully preserved in the conversion to offices, with even the dumb waiter hatches left in place!

In May 1979 an order was received from the National Coal Board for a two mile underground electrification scheme at Gedling Colliery, Nottinghamshire. The BW overhead designs included a large number of the old trolleybus fittings and the locomotives were fitted with mining pantographs of the older, diamond pattern. This was a major advance in the design of coal mines but the system was in full production for only five years before closure.

Activities in the Company were on the increase, and Beyer, Peacock decided the time had come to sell. On 12th June 1979 Brecknell, Willis was bought by Lord and Lady Tanlaw, under the banner name of The Fandstan Electric Group. Lord Tanlaw was an active participant in electric traction and alternative energy, and was to encourage BW into a number of developments. Soon after taking control of BW, he also purchased Braune Batricar, based at Stroud, manufacturing light electric vehicles for the elderly and infirmed.

Meanwhile, on the other side of the world, Victoria Railways in Australia had ordered 200 Highreach units. The contract was based again on some local manufacture, so a local BW offshoot was set up, Austbreck, to assemble parts shipped over from Chard. Austbreck was situated in Melbourne, and was able to supply large numbers of pantographs, particularly to Victoria Railways, over the succeeding years.

The work with British Rail's research department had gone well, and it was decided to fit BW highspeed pantographs to the new Advanced Passenger Trains, then beginning trial running. The units performed well, and the trial runs saw speeds gradually increased under test conditions on the west coast main line during June 1979. Finally, it was decided that the time was right for an attempt on the British speed record, and in July the trial train reached a speed of 162.5mph on the descent of Beattock in Scotland. BW staff were on board to observe, and the figure was a record for British traction.

In 1980 once again, however, the technical advances were using up funds and performance was suffering. Orders for industrial equipment had fallen sharply after the British Steel strike in April. There were a number of urgent maintenance jobs being postponed, particularly on the buildings, which were in need of repair. The main Denings building roof leaked, and there was a problem with flooding in the yard outside. Following projected losses for the first half of 1980, coupled with very low order input the Company had to reduce costs. It was decided that, in order to maintain employment for the majority, 18 employees would be made redundant - some voluntarily. Into this uncertain environment a new technical manager was recruited - from British Rail! Tony Hobbs had worked on the development of the Advanced Passenger Train and was one of the key members of the BR team working on the highspeed development of the BW pantograph.

During the latter part of 1980 a BW pantograph on South African Railways was tested at high speed and reached 210 km/hr. SAR was one of the largest railway systems in the world, and there were six thousand pantographs in service at that time, mainly of European manufacture. Also in South Africa, the Company also achieved another technical step forward with the successful operation of twin pole pantographs at both Palabora and Sishen Mines, where the diesel-electric trucks were able to save valuable fuel oil by using electricity from twin pole overhead in the climb out of the mines. The prototypes had worked well, and after all the development work BW were confident of receiving the main order. The work was badly needed.

The news from South Africa, when it came, was bad. The whole order for mining pantographs had gone to a German competitor, Stemmann Technik, and with the situation becoming desperate, in March 1981 BW went onto a three-day working week which was to last two difficult months.

In June 1981 an order for trolleypole equipment was received for Calcutta Tramways - the first trolleypole order for many years. The irony was that it was not for a BW design, but one produced originally by Dick, Kerr and Co, and passed to BW by GEC. The West Yorkshire PTE contacted the Company in July 1981. They were considering the reintroduction of trolleybuses, and asked BW to submit proposals for the design and installation of an overhead system. This was the first of three abortive attempts to reintroduce trolleybuses into the UK in the last twenty years of the century. The new Dublin Metro produced an order for 46 pantographs.

The service prototype BR/BW highspeed pantograph was returned to BW for detailed examination after 200,000 miles of service on locomotive No.86244 on the west coast main line, and twelve further units were built for extended trial.

By the autumn of 1981 BW pantographs were now in service in Australia, Eire, Italy, Norway, Britain, and the USA, and further trials followed in on the Hong Kong Mass Transit Railway, ATM Milan, Seoul Metro, and the Rotterdam Tramways. An Amtrak highspeed pantograph had completed 50,000 miles of service running on the north east corridor without incident. BW had supplied to Dutch railways a trial pantograph for their 1500V operation using parts developed from other projects, as the Engineering department became more confident with the product. Design and manufacture was completed in four weeks!

All the work with pantographs tended to dominate the news but the industrial side of the Company was still winning significant orders. The steelworks at Port Talbot were unloading iron ore from ships and these were moved to the blast furnaces by a set of bunker cars powered by an old third rail system. BW designed and installed a twin pole copper Brecktrack system as a replacement and this was installed in February 1983. The exposed site, 80ft up on gantries with the cold winter wind blowing in from the Atlantic, was not the most popular installation job in the Company at the time! (This system was actually installed twice, for the following year the whole system was stolen!)

In January 1983 Fandstan Electric bought back the two fields adjacent to 'The Elms', thus restoring the land assets to the position in 1947 prior to the merger with Anti-Attrition.

Electric Truck production was restarted in February 1983, using three standard models, but they were the existing BW designs - there was still no technical discussions or overlap with Batricar, within the Fandstan group. Some good orders followed, notably with Eurolift, which seemed to promise some growth. Later that year ideas began to emerge for a product for the fairground business - an electric go-kart, and three prototype vehicles were built and demonstrated on a test track built on land outside 'The Elms', but interest from the market was limited and the idea was dropped. The vehicles and track were scrapped but some publicity material survives from this unusual project.

A visitor to the drawing office in 1983 would have seen the office in much the same state it had been a hundred years earlier, with all drawings done by hand on boards, and with primitive copying and filing systems. This year, however, modern technology was introduced, in the form of a microfilm reader, which was expected to drastically simplify the access to drawings and printing work. One of the tasks undertaken was to microfilm the older drawings inherited from the past, including many Brecknell, Munro and Rogers designs. The originals were drawn on tracing paper or linen and by this period were becoming fragile.

New pantograph equipment was now on trial with Oslo Tramways, and ATAC in Rome, and a pre-production unit was sent to Bombardier in Canada, to be evaluated on their test track where new cars were commissioned. Further Bombardier orders followed. A new joint development with BR was proposed to cover medium speed pantograph design, and was approved by the Department of Trade and Industry for grant funding. Unfortunately, BR subsequently withdrew its interest and BW was left to proceed on its own.

Fifteen pantographs were now in service with British Rail on Class 87 locomotives, and there were experiments to increase the speed of these locomotives from 100 to 110mph, making use of the superior current collection achieved with the Brecknell design. There was further elation in May 1984 when the 1000th single arm pantograph was completed, and BW had a healthy order book stretching for three months into the future. The Brecktrack shrouded conductor system received approval from the CEGB after elaborate short circuit testing in their development laboratory. These triumphs were notable, but still not contributing to the Company finances. Throughout 1983 and into 1984 the financial affairs were unstable. A small profit one month was followed by a large loss the next, and the performance was further damaged by the British docks strike in the spring of 1984. This held up dispatch of pantographs for Holland and South Africa, and there was a direct effect on business associated with dockside cranes which would never recover. It was this strike, coming soon after the steel strike in 1980 that hastened the demise of the Company's industrial division.

Photo 6.1 A new product, Brecktrack, was launched in 1974 as a direct competitor to several existing conductor bar designs, and used in the crane, industrial and peoplemover markets. This photograph shows an early installation in Space Decks in 1974.

Photo 6.2 The new single arm pantograph, designed by Bob Whiteley, is successfully tested on the Seaton tramway in 1974. (courtesy David Wheadon).

Photo 6.3 The Switzerland Exhibition in 1974, featured Brecktrack and the new pantograph, as well as festoon systems and trolley wire fittings.

Photo 6.4 Third rail collector for the Toronto underground system. The first units were supplied in 1953; this was the third batch made in February 1974.
(courtesy David Wheadon)

Photo 6.5 Ken Williams and a colleague assemble the first prototype Tyne and Wear pantograph in the Denings building at Chard, February 1974. (courtesy David Wheadon)

Photo 6.7 The first major order for the single-arm pantograph was for the Tyne and Wear metro 1976, with 100 pantographs supplied. This photograph shows the first trial unit on the test track near Newcastle.

Photo 6.6 Gordon Down, Tony White and Sean Crossman at work on pantograph assembly, 1975.

Photo 6.8 Local manufacture of pantographs started in the USA in 1979. In the centre is Sean Crossman, who spent time with the USA team, and later returned to Chard as BW Sales Manager.

Photo 6.9 First visit of the new owners, Lord and Lady Tanlaw, to Chard, 5th July 1979, with Len Clampett, the Production Director, and the prototype high speed pantograph. On the right is Tony White, who was to rise to Managing Director in 1997.

Photo 6.10 A conveyer system for Thorn EMI being assembled at Chard, inside the old Denings building in 1979. In the background can be seen the production line for electric trucks.

Photo 6.11 A large contract for Brecktrack in Corby steelworks, 1979. Note the use of polyester insulators to provide secondary insulation in the severe environment. With the reorganisation of British Steel, however, Corby was closed.

Photo 6.12 An AEM7 locomotive fitted with a BW high speed pantograph on trial at the USA's Department of Transport's Pueblo test facility in August 1980.

Photo 6.13 In 1980, Batricar produced a series of new literature, and one posed view is shown here. The people were models, employed for the day.

Photo 6.14 Pantographs and overhead were installed in Gedling Colliery in 1981. This was the largest underground installation the Company had tackled, but within just a few years the whole workings were abandoned.

Photo 6.15 Locomotive 86244 with the British Rail trial high speed unit in service on the West Coast main line at Euston in 1981.

Photo 6.16 A high speed Pantograph on one of the pre-production advanced passenger trains. During 1979 a speed of 162.5mph was reached in trials between Lockerbie and Beattock (courtesy British Rail).

Photo 6.17 The third and fourth rail setup at Port Talbot, South Wales, to supply the iron ore bunker cars. This is the first system installed in 1983; after a period of disuse the entire system was stolen, and had to be replaced!

Photo 6.18 A first order for 31 electrically-raised pantographs for Rotterdam, in 1983, was followed by further orders in later years.

Photo 6.19 In late 1983 a new prototype truck was produced at Chard, and the unit is seen here under test, driven by stores manager Betty McHardy. This was the largest truck to be made by the Company, but it never entered volume production.

Photo 6.20 Staff on the occasion of the completion of the 1000th single arm pantograph, May 1984. (courtesy David Wheadon).

Photo 6.21 Diesel-electric hybrid trucks at Palabora, South Africa, 1984. Loaded trucks use the overhead wires at 1200 V dc for the climb out of the open pit mine. The figure in blue overalls and yellow hard hat is Technical Director, Tony Hobbs.

CHAPTER 7 - Conductor Rail Systems

The Tyne and Wear metro in Newcastle had turned out a great success, and planners in London were considering a similar urban metro system as part of the plans to regenerate the docklands area in east London. The route of the line was to start from beside Fenchurch Street station, and run out to the docks area, with a branch to Mile End, where there would be some street running. The power supply would be by overhead wire. The developers, however, became nervous about introducing a new street-running tram to the London traffic, and the Mile End portion was scrapped; and some artist impressions of the overhead system were so ungainly that GEC, the main contractor, was asked to consider alternatives. GEC therefore approached BW to consider a third rail system.

Third rail systems have existed for as long as electrification itself - the very first public electric train was powered by a third rail in 1879. Brecknell, Munro and Rogers had produced some third rail system components in the 1920's, but had never had much expertise in third rail design. Nevertheless, the BW development team sketched out ideas, and with the help of GEC, an experimental setup was made in an old power station complex at Kearsley, Lancashire. This was designed as a three-phase, top-running steel rail system. This gave both BW and GEC confidence, and in August 1984 outline proposals were made for a three-phase side-running system for the London contract which would be for twenty-two single track kilometres.

The formal order for the third rail system at London Docklands was received from GEC Transportation in October 1984 and at £1.25million was the largest in the Company's recent history. After intense technical discussions the three phase system was abandoned, and in its place was a design consisting of a single third rail at 750 volts, with the vehicle shoes collecting current from the underside - a new system for Britain. The contract included vehicle shoegear and fuses and most importantly, interfaces with the rolling stock and civil engineering disciplines. For the first time in many years BW would be involved in major project work, with staff travelling regularly to site and technical meetings, and generally supporting the client.

Although the Kearsley setup had been with steel rail, the BW engineering team promoted the concept of high conductivity aluminium rails. This allowed the use of a smaller and lighter rail than those made of steel, which was an important benefit in the reduced space available on the Docklands system. After some searching of the market, a design was settled using a stainless steel strip bonded to the aluminium. This was a process invented by Alusingen, a German aluminium company, and this was the start of an association between the two organisations in the succeeding years.

Pantographs were on trial in two new locations: the state railways of Finland, and the STIB and SNCV operations in Belgium, and in September 1984 the company received the first phase of an order for SICARTSA - a steel complex in Mexico. This order for crane electrification would last five years.

News of the Company's involvement in third rail design spread through the industry. BW was contacted by Henry Boot, who had recently obtained the contract for trackwork on the new metro system in Singapore, which included a substantial portion of third rail design and supply. Tony Hobbs visited Singapore with representatives of Henry Boot, to make proposals to the client for the third rail system. These were based on conventional technology in Europe but using aluminium conductor rails to reduce losses along the line. The association with Alusingen was helpful here, for the German rail had been chosen by the consultant in Singapore, and the joint proposals were accepted.

The financial results for 1984 were a significant improvement on previous years, and at long last a profit was made. The announcement was made by Ken McQueen at the annual gathering of staff before the Christmas shutdown, and his speech was given while standing on a packing crate in the cavernous emptiness of the former Norringtons showroom, recently absorbed back into BW.

There were now four operating groups within BW - pantographs, third rail, vehicles and industrial. Each had a lead engineer, and each had its own costing system with all internal staff hours and materials, and external purchases and sub-contracts, separately accounted to the appropriate division. This was to be the accounting model which has remained up until the present time. All staff were transferred to a monthly-paid basis, and attempts were made to unify the hours worked. At this time the Works started earlier in the morning than the offices, and worked longer hours. In addition, there were a number of part-time staff. It was a difficult and frustrating system, and gradually it was accepted that some common hours of working were essential. It was to take 18 months of confusion and mixed working as different departments one by one adjusted their hours; but by the summer of 1986 all staff were working 37½ hours, arranged as Monday - Thursday four long days and a shortened Friday.

The Railway industry was quick off the mark with the new discipline of Quality Assurance and BW would have to follow suit if it were to continue to trade effectively. Following the appointment of the Company's first quality manager in March 1985, application for BS 5750 approval proceeded. This was a tricky process, involving the production of large amounts of documentation, but the team was already well prepared and the application was made in good time.

Several decades had passed since London Transport and BW had worked together, but plans were afoot for the manufacture of a new generation of trains for the Central line. Metro Cammell had the contract for two prototype trains and approached BW to develop suitable shoegear. By summer 1985 this work was proceeding apace. The designs were heavy and massive, reflecting the LUL policy on shoegear, and made a stark contrast in the engineering development area with the new Docklands collectors being developed alongside.

The discussions with the Singapore consultants had proceeded, and after a further meeting in Singapore in March 1985 BW signed a contract with Henry Boot for the third rail system for the Singapore MRT covering development, supply and installation. At £5.5million this was the largest single order in the Company's history at that time. This massive contract required careful management, and Ken McQueen left Chard to supervise the work personally. Tony Hobbs became BW's Managing Director, and he made it clear to all staff that the Company's general trading position was not good, and that had it not been for the Singapore and Docklands contracts substantial contraction of its operations would have been necessary. Industrial equipment sales continued to decline; pantograph business was growing only slowly, and was in any event insufficient to sustain the general operations at their present level. It was the new third rail business on which the future would depend.

Summer 1985 was a busy time for the new third rail team at Chard. Not only was there the effort of new designs for the Docklands conductor rail and shoegear, with all the attendent prototype and test work, but there was a huge effort in submitting designs to the MRT in Singapore. Four separate visits were made to Singapore in 1985 to gain approval of the designs, each accompanied by massive movements of paperwork between BW, Henry Boot, and the client. The effort was made all the more arduous by the number of drawing prints required, so that each submission process involved the printing of some

150 drawings, some of large size, with 12 copies of each. One communication advance was a dramatic help, however. This was the first contract where messages from abroad were received at Chard by 'facsimile machine'. Previously the Company's formal foreign communications were by telex, with the BW receptionist in Chard handling around 200 incoming and outgoing messages a week. The new system simplified matters dramatically, and the first message received at Chard was David Hartland's visit report from Singapore in March 1985 - and that was received on the Space Decks facs next door since BW had not yet moved over to the new technology! It would be another four years before the facs machine finally ousted the telex machine from the reception area at Chard. The strict views of the Singapore consultant on expansion joint design pushed the BW team into exploring ideas for these devices, and the result was a novel unit which allowed free mechanical movement without any sliding electrical contact. The design has been used on its third rail systems ever since.

Prior to Lord Tanlaw's Fandstan Electric group, Stemmann Technik had been strong competition to BW. Now it was half owned by Lord Tanlaw, and it was time to begin to establish some inter-company discussions and make agreements about the marketplace. Lord Tanlaw's instructions in October 1985 outlined how the two organisations would work together. Where there were clashes of interest, particularly in terms of pantographs, BW would define the policy. A first priority was to achieve trials of BW style pantographs on the German Railway system. (This, however, was to take 12 years to achieve).

After a whole year in the design stage, installation started at London Docklands in February 1986 with a team drawn from the works at Chard. The lightweight third rail was suitable for installation with only a four-man gang, and work proceeded quickly, with third rail being laid as soon as the trackwork was ready. Bad weather, however, disrupted progress in April, and there were difficulties in the deliveries of conductor rail from Germany, but by the summer the depot was complete and work was advancing on the main lines.

In June 1986 the company achieved a milestone by becoming Quality Approved to BS 5750 Part 1, covering design, manufacture, and installation activities. This was an unusual and forward step in those days, and Tony Hobbs thanked the Quality Manager John Ladbrook and all staff for their efforts in this respect. He had been personally informed by the British Standards Institute that BW was the first company for several years to qualify without reservation. Also in 1986 the Batricar factory closed in Stroud and all production was moved to Chard, set up in the former Denings building.

In December 1986 Ken McQueen left the Company. His friendly, personal manner was already missed by staff in Chard after his year in Singapore, and the departure was a further disappointment. In succeeding years, however, he was to visit BW as an independent consultant on several other urban metro projects. The same month, a new computer system was installed at Chard to handle accounts and salaries, but there were still no computers involved in any design or production planning activities anywhere in the Works.

Meanwhile, back on British Rail, the performance and maintenance savings with the BW unit were becoming noticed at last. The Stone-Faiveley pantographs, which formed the vast majority of units in BR service, were experiencing generic problems with their head design, and BW designed and tried a new head system to fit. This was to extend the lives of the Faiveley units for some years.

At Docklands, the first vehicle had arrived from the German factory, and for the first time the BW shoegear made contact with the BW conductor rail. All was well, and in March 1987 BW staff had the use of vehicle No.2 for some high-speed trials around the system.

Performance of the shoegear was monitored during the three-day test programme, and glowing reports were produced. It was clear that the progressive lightweight collector design, with its rubber-mounted shoe, was coping well in the environment and the new collector was worth pushing for other projects. The design was modified for Rotterdam and Helsinki, and collectors were supplied to these systems.

In June 1987 the first electric multiple unit was run at Singapore, with much pomp and ceremony, and later that summer BW staff were treated to a day out on the Docklands line, giving the chance for the staff to see the end results of their labours in the new third rail business.

The prototype trains on London Underground were working well, and LUL approached BW for some further work. This took the form of a development project with the aim of making an altogether new type of shoegear which could be used on future rolling stock. A design was evolved which used direct air pressure, rather than gravity, to apply the contact force, and three assemblies with their associated shoebeams were manufactured and fitted to a Jubilee line train, and run at speeds up to 55 mph. Performance was dramatically improved over existing shoegear, but the perceived complications of direct air control led to the project being abandoned by LUL. It provided useful experience, however, and led in part to the work on the 'A' stock and Jubilee line shoegear a few years later.

By the end of 1988 the third rail contracts had boosted both turnover and profit. The original Docklands system was being expanded, and the experiences in Singapore was being promoted in Taiwan, where another metro system was being constructed. Lord Tanlaw's investments were at last bringing a healthy return, but only after ten years under his ownership. It was as well that he had been patient.

Photo 7.1 Lunchbreak for the Docklands installation staff in June 1986. The Unimog vehicle was used for the installation, there being no road access to the working sites.

Photo 7.2 Coming hard on the heels of the Docklands contract, was the vastly greater contract for the Singapore Mass Transit electrification. This was a third rail system, based on European practice, led by a German design consortium. BW had all design and manufacture responsibility, and supervised installation on site. The photograph shows work on the test track at Bishan Depot. Labour was never in short supply!

Photo 7.3 Richard Whitefield with the battery trolley used for electric continuity tests at Docklands, July 1986. The umbrella kept the sun and the rain off the instruments (but also attracted humorous comments!)

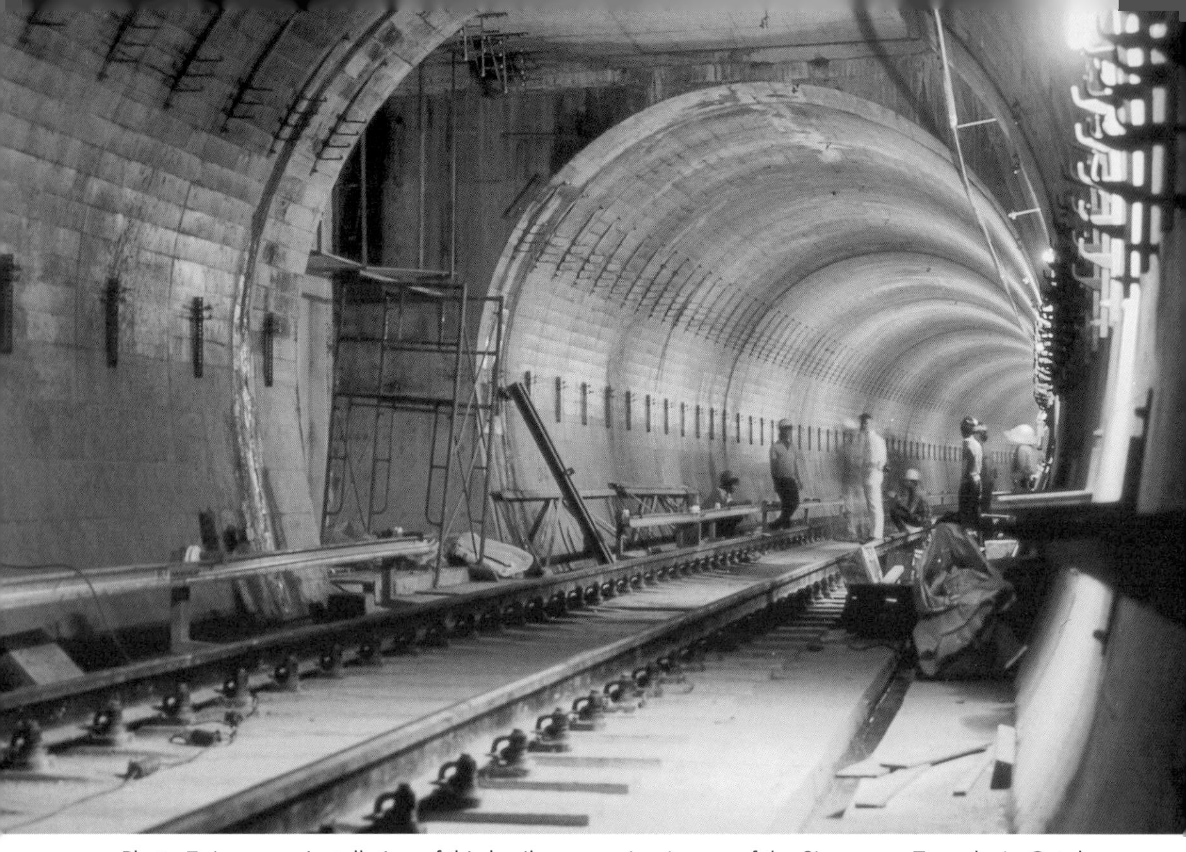

Photo 7.4 Installation of third rail progressing in one of the Singapore Tunnels, in October 1986. To the right is BW site engineer Jeff Thorne, who subsequently led the marketing operation for the Far East in Taipei.

Photo 7.5 This photograph, taken during commissioning tests in March 1987, shows DLR vehicle 02 being overtaken by a class 86 on an up Norwich train, providing a nice contrast between overhead and third rail contact systems. A Stone-Faiveley pantograph provides the overhead power to the locomotive, but within 12 months Brecknell, Willis units had started to replace the Faiveley type on this region of British Rail. It is ironic to note that this route was the last British line to receive BW pantographs, but had been the first to use them on trial runs in 1974.

Photo 7.6 A particularly prestigious BW job in 1987 was the Brecktrack system installed to power the hanger doors of the Concorde shed at Heathrow Airport.

Photo 7.7 The new Golf Kart design, masterminded by BW engineering team, on display for publicity purposes. It dismantled completely for transport in the boot of a Ford Cortina or Sierra of the time.

Photo 7.8 This picture shows how the Docklands line has been aligned carefully to pass parallel through the very cramped bridge girders. It was this bridge which limited the whole conductor rail design for the system - the cost of widening the bridge would have been prohibitive, so the conductor rail structure gauge was designed around this girder clearance. Photograph taken March 1987.

Photo 7.9 Test train at Docklands, March 1987. On board is Bill Southcombe talking to the driver.

Photo 7.10 'The Elms', newly restored. Photograph June 1987. Note the Company cars of the period.

Photo 7.11 A development contract with LUL produced this trial shoegear mounted on a Jubilee line train. The complications of direct air actuation were not accepted, however, and the project was abandoned.

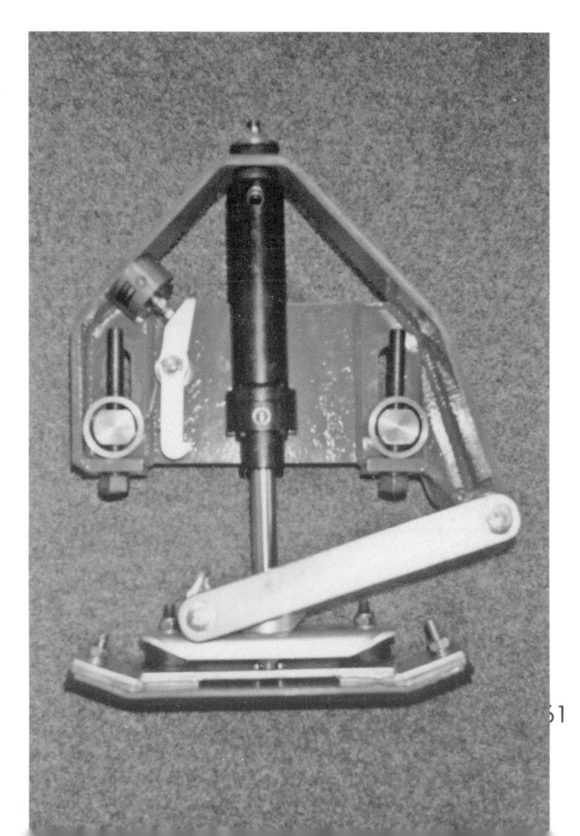

Photo 7.12 The first trial run of a Singapore train took place at the Bishan test track in June 1987.

Photo 7.13 Short-circuit bars were a new product for the Company, as a part of the third rail work. They are intended for application, in an emergency, to a live third rail. This picture shows a live test under carefully controlled conditions, in the tunnel at Bank.

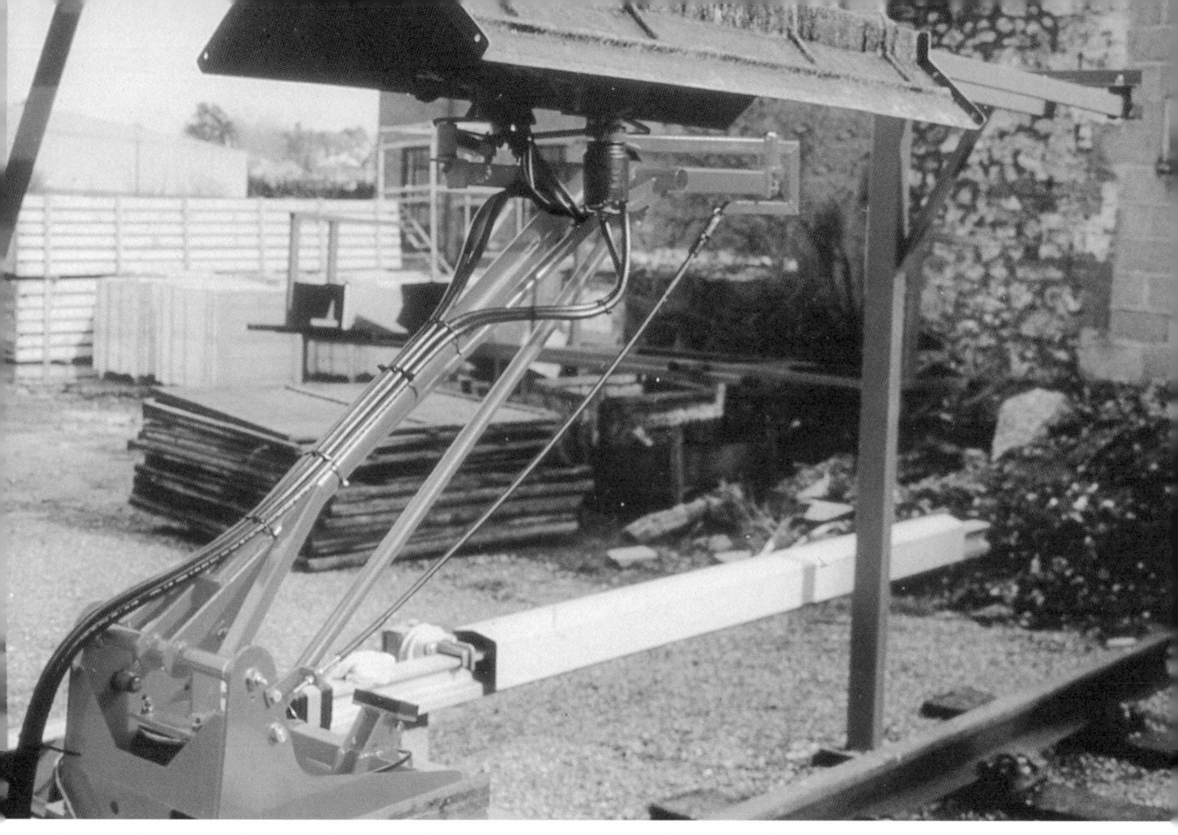

Photo 7.14 Current collector supplied to construction locomotives for the Channel Tunnel in May 1988.

Photo 7.15 By June 1988 there was only one model of Batricar in regular production. Here Hardy Stoodley and Anthony Galpin are testing two vehicles straight from the line.

Photo 7.16 The Batricar Production line, with a batch of 'Alpha' units under construction.

Chapter 8 - Eurostar and Aluminium Conductor Rails

British Rail had been using steel conductor rails on its third rail systems in Liverpool and the Southern region, since the earliest days. They were simple to use and install, but suffered from low electrical conductivity. Other systems around the world were experimenting with aluminium, and the BW experiences in Singapore led to British Rail gradually taking an interest. In 1988, BW installed a trial using Alusingen rail at two sites on the southern area, at Upwey, near the site of the former Wishing Well Halt, and later at Weybridge on the down fast line. Initial results were pleasing, and a contract was awarded to BW to supply and install 5 miles of rail for the Botley-Fareham electrification scheme. The low resistance rail enabled a reduction in the required number of substations, leading to a healthy saving on overall electrification costs. Within a few months however, there were signs of problems emerging. The Weybridge trial rail suffered damage, and the basic design of the rail, with its co-extruded molecular bonding of stainless steel, was at fault. The supplier was unhelpful, and with such a fundamental difficulty emerging, it was time for BW to develop its own design of aluminium rail. After various brainstorming sessions, a design emerged based on welding two stainless steel lengths, each of letter 'J' in section, to the upper surface of the aluminium. A short test rig of 2m length was produced, and initial test results were so encouraging that BR took an interest. The first trial was installed at Woking, on the up fast line, on midsummer's night 1990. Patents were filed in many countries, and a series of endurance tests were undertaken to prove the new design. The rights to the patents were purchased from the BW employee for the princely sum of one United States Dollar!

The Channel Tunnel boring operations were underway, and on the British side two short tunnels had been built to access the main tunnel workings and transport spoil away. These tunnels were on a steep gradient, and temporary tracks were installed, with electric locomotives supplied from a two-pole overhead using Brecktrack bar and a purpose-built pantograph-type collector. After some development, the system worked well and BW was invited to bid for the main tunnelling contracts on the British and French sides of the tunnel, to electrify the entire tunnel with overhead and equip all the contractor's locomotives with collectors. The BW trial work had proven the system, and the development team at Chard were well respected, but unfortunately the French competitor was prepared to offer a very low price and he won the work on both sides of the Channel. BW's development work had been in vain, and the loss of such a prestigious contract was a major blow to the organisation.

A minor enquiry was received in 1989 for shoegear, this time on British Rail, where the existing licensed manufacturer was in difficulties and wished to withdraw from production. There was some reluctance in BW to take on this kind of 'jobbing' work to someone else's design, especially with such a heavy type of shoegear, but in the end it was agreed to tool up and manufacture the first batch, for the Class 319 Thameslink trains. This small contract, however, was one of the most significant ever achieved by the Company, for it was to lead directly to mass production of the existing BR design, and to allow BW to introduce firstly its own improvements, and later, novel designs on BR and Railtrack for the major rolling stock builds over the subsequent 15 years. It also gave BW an entry into a dramatic, international project.

The building work on the Channel Tunnel was well advanced, but there was no progress on the construction of a new line from Folkestone to London and it was becoming obvious that the new passenger trains due to run through the tunnel would have to reach London on existing lines, taking current from the third rail. There was a strong political will that the development work for the trains should be spread between the nations involved, and the main British contractor, GEC, was forming a joint venture with its French counterpart Alsthom, later to become a single company. Following this lead, BW formed a joint venture with its old French rival, Faiveley, to supply the complete current collection package. It was agreed that Faiveley would provide its own pantograph design suited to the French system, while a second, BW highspeed unit would be fitted to the locomotives to suit the dc system in Belgium. The shoegear for BR lines would nominally be a joint development, although BW's background in shoegear meant that the design work was based in Chard. Prototype assemblies were manufactured and fitted to a special test train which ran on the southern area for two years, with various high speed tests along the way. After some modifications, the first equipment ran on a Eurostar train in 1990 and the trains entered service in 1994. Test running up to 106mph between Dollands Moor and the new depot at North Pole proved the shoegear and demonstrated a reserve of speed which, sadly, has not been used in service.

The east coast main line electrification between King's Cross and Edinburgh was completed in 1989 and the new train service would be pulled by the new Class 91 locomotive from GEC, powered by a BW pantograph. Trial runs showed the performance to be good enough to confirm the planned operating speed of 140mph. In fact it was so good that a high speed run was planned to challenge the British speed record, reached ten years earlier by the APT. On 17th September 1989 locomotive 91019 reached 162mph with the BW Chief Engineer on board, but this was half a mile per hour short of the previous record.

After success on the trial BW conductor rail at Woking, BW won the contract for 3 miles of conductor rail for the Waterloo and City line in London. This included installation, and special features for turnouts on the negative rail on this line which runs under the River Thames. Even larger was the follow-up contract with BR to supply 40 kilometres of rail and insulators for the Chester - Hooton and Ellesmere Port electrification on Merseyside. For this, a new range of porcelain insulators was developed which allowed rapid installation and adjustment to achieve an accurate rail profile.

The new railway to the airport at Hong Kong was a prestigious job for 1991 and the Company was able to provide pantographs and continue its excellent relationship with the local operators.

Photo 8.1 In 1989 large orders were obtained for the manufacture of a 1980 BR design, and various improvements were made as the shoegear was supplied to successive rolling stock manufacture in the following five years.

Photo 8.2 Bill Southcombe and Laurie Hanks (BR) at 02.58 on July 3rd 1988 at the installation of the first aluminium/stainless steel conductor rail on British Rail, near Upwey, Dorset. The first train passed through the section at 03.01. The rail used was a co-extruded system manufactured by Alusingen of Germany.

Photo 8.3 Gas tensioner on the overhead line at Brussels' tramway.

Photo 8.4 Class 91 No. 91019 stands at Grantham before the attempt at the British speed record, 17th September 1989.

Photo 8.5 Batricar float at Taunton Carnival. This was to win several prizes on the South Somerset carnival circuit in 1989.

Photo 8.6 Staff Picture, on the last day before the Christmas break, December 1989. With 143 staff, there were almost too many for one photograph.
(Photograph courtesy David Wheadon).

Photo 8.7 Class 73 No. 73205 (providing the traction power) and 83301 (with TMST bogies and Brecknell, Willis shoegear) stand at Woking on trials for Channel tunnel through trains. BW staff were involved with high speed trials of the shoegear between Woking and Basingstoke where speeds of up to 100 mph were proven. The test train continued in service for two years, evaluating BW shoegear, and provided the essential trial running before the main manufacture for the Eurostar trains.

Photo 8.8 During 1990 the British Government consistently refused to apply public money to a high speed rail link from the Channel Tunnel to London. Exasperation was running high when this cartoon appeared in the London Evening Standard for 13th June 1990. Note the correctly reproduced BW trolley pole and fittings! The caption reads "would passengers arriving from Paris please transfer to the No.12 tram for Kings Cross!" (courtesy London Evening Standard).

Photo 8.9 The joint venture for aluminium rail development is signed by BR Southern General Manager John Nelson and Lord Tanlaw in 1990.

Photo 8.10 BW pantographs were used on the Manchester Trams, seen here in 1991.

Photo 8.11 View of the rail production line at Chard 1993. The two stainless steel J-sections are horizontal and welded in the middle of the railhead.

Chapter 9 - 100 years of Electrification

1994 was the 100th anniversary of electrification in the Company, but the year will really be remembered as the year of the Jubilee line extension. BW staff were busily engaged with design of the shoegear for the new trains, using experience gained from previous work with London Underground, and by the summer trial units were in service on the Metropolitan line at high speed. The new design made extensive use of investment cast stainless steel components, to reduce the reliance on painting or plating processes, and minimise machining. The performance of the lightweight units was significantly better than existing LUL shoegear, and there was follow-up work on the Northern line with a similar design. Interestingly, the Northern line shoegear was sold with an agreed maintenance provision for 15 years, approximating to BW leasing the equipment to GEC Alsthom and LUL at a fixed price. This was a real case of the Company putting its money where its mouth was!

Meanwhile, the conductor rail system, all 100 kilometres of it, was up for tender. The specification required the use of molecularly-bonded aluminium/stainless rail, but after intense lobbying, and after studies of the incident at Weybridge, LUL finally agreed to change the specification, and the new BW aluminium rail was written in. This was major news indeed. Not only did this tremendous order give continuous work for the rail shop for almost two years, but it complemented nicely the work done on the shoegear, because the usually complex process of interfacing between the rolling stock and infrastructure teams on the project reduced to a discussion across the drawing office in Chard!

Chard town was a little behind the times, and had no large supermarket in the area. The large retailers were all interested in setting up an outlet, and the extensive BW site attracted close attention. To outsiders, including apparently the local council, this was an old industrial site, under-utilised, and crying out for development into a shiny new supermarket, bringing many new jobs to the town. The Company management were bombarded with attempts to purchase the whole site and a study was done as to the realistic costs of moving the whole operation to a greenfield area elsewhere. There were even attempts to sway opinion at owner level. To the credit of the Company team, and probably the long-term wealth of the town, it was decided not to move, but to retain ownership of the complete site. The supermarket would have to be built elsewhere. (Eventually Tesco built a supermarket on the site of the Bass warehouse, itself on the old station site).

As if to consolidate the decision to stay, it was time to spruce up the whole Works. The central quadrangle, site of the machine shop in the 1950s, was levelled and planted. The former packing and stores area was extended in a style copying the existing 1920's building, and a test shop was build spanning the gap to the engineering unit. Part of one of the Elms fields was taken up with a car park to house the growing number of cars used by employees to reach the workplace. The original foundry gatehouse building was refurbished, and the bell tower restored - with working bell sounding the start and finish times. A new tarmac road was built around the site, following the old Tapstone Lane route and the drive up to 'The Elms', and a large brick gateway, with wrought iron entrance gates was placed at East Street, across where Tapstone Lane used to meander through the site. The large assembly hall was extended, complete with overhead crane, to cope with the increasing trainborne assembly work.

The year 1994 could not pass without some reference to the hundred years in the electric traction business. The Company calendar for 1994 was already published as a collection of old BW photographs with the modern counterpart, and in June 1994 it was decided to celebrate with a large fete and dinner for invited guests. The proceedings were opened by the local MP and leader of the Liberal Party, Paddy Ashdown, and The Works was thrown open to visitors, friends and family who were shown around the displays by the staff. A photographic history of the Company was set up, and the fete featured pony rides, a coconut shy and even a miniature railway. And best of all, the sun shone all day! In the evening there was a lavish dinner for invited guests in a large marquee. David Gillan, from the Railway Industry Association, gave a humorous speech, praising BW on its achievements, and looking into the future; Lord Tanlaw responded for the Company, thanking the guests for coming and pledging another hundred years for the good of public transport. The night was concluded with a dramatic and lengthy firework show, which drew gasps from the observers, (but also complaints from the Chard locality!).

The Company was becoming well-known for supply of aluminium conductor rail, but the summer of 1994 saw work start on a 40km steel conductor rail system for a new metro in Ankara, the Turkish capital. The client, SNC-Lavalin, was based in Canada, and there was much shuttling between the three countries during the contract bid work. The main steel rail (all 3000 tons of it) went direct from the steelworks to Turkey, but BW received an amount for conversion into ramps and expansion joints, and an area was set up in the Denings building fitted with overhead cranes to deal with the steel lengths. The contract went well, and relations were formed with both the Canadian engineers and local Turkish companies which would be useful in the future.

The end of 1994 saw a few significant changes. Electric vehicle production was continuing, with a new 'Golf Kart' design which initially sold well. The whole operation at Chard was geared to a production rate of around 8 vehicles per day, and formed a useful sink of labour to cope with the peaks and troughs of the railway business. While the manufacturing was well developed, however, the sales were always tricky, this business not fitting in at all with the existing BW range of agents. In addition, the 'Golf Karts' failed to gain acceptance on the majority of British golf courses, and the future became most uncertain. Worse still, sales were suddenly affected in 1994 by an influx of low-cost designs from the Far East. In December 1994 it was decided to sell the entire operation - designs, tooling, and stock, and all electric vehicle work ceased. At the same time, the railway side was reformed into two distinct operating divisions - one covering the rolling stock business (Trainborne Equipment) and the other the fixed infrastructure (Electrification Systems). All staff were allocated to one or other division, with a separate engineering team to serve both groups. This organisation was to continue for a few years, before it was realised that the system limited flexibility and a number of functions were unnecessarily duplicated, and the Company reverted to the more traditional management format.

Insulating materials were an essential part of Company products, and for some time there had been a small group in BW making fibreglass products, boosted in later years by the electric vehicles business. The market appeared buoyant, and the Group felt the need to expand into more focused composites activity. In 1994 the Fandstan Group bought the Wiltshire company Strachan and Fox, and brought the fibreglass business into the Group. Much work was generated in train internal panels, and one prestigious job undertaken in 1995 was the production of driving cab ends for the Jubilee and Northern line trains. These were complex phenolic mouldings and at the height of production five complete train ends were being produced per day using resin injection techniques. BW was responsible for the development work, including some dramatic high-speed impact tests with missiles to prove the strength of the train cabs. (Eventually the operation was moved to Chard on a separate site at Millfield, and continues to trade as BW Composites.)

Photo 9.1 Extension to the old packing shop to accommodate the machine shop, 1993.

Photo 9.2 Extension to the main assembly hall 1993 (compare with photograph 5.11).

Photo 9.3 Marquees at the Centenary, erected on the field adjacent to 'The Elms'.

Photo 9.4 Opening of the Centenary Celebrations, June 1994. From left to right, Lady and Lord Tanlaw, Helen Ingram, Mr and Mrs Paddy Ashdown, Tony and Pat Hobbs.

Photo 9.5 The Cake Stall: left to right, Tracey Cain, Audrey Follett, Vicky Heavyside and Val Sparks.

Photo 9.6 David Hartland and David Ingram (from British Rail) during a break in their driving turns on the miniature railway.

Photo 9.7 Steel conductor rails are unloaded at the Ankara metro construction site.

Photo 9.8. Martin Sheppard assembling the first production runs of Jubilee line shoegear.

Photo 9.9 A major job in 1995 was the design of shoegear for General Electric in America, for trains running into new York.

Photo 9.10 BW pantograph in service on the X2000 train in USA. This reached a speed of 155mph on test runs.

Photo 9.11 On 22nd March 1995 two members of the engineering staff retired. Les Clark, responsible for industrial equipment design, had served 16 years, while Audrey Follet started in 1945 working with Arnold Willis, and completed 42 years with one break. Also in the picture are Tony Hobbs and David Hartland. (courtesy David Wheadon).

Photo 9.12. Conductor Rail installation completed at Stratford Market Depot, Jubilee line extension.

Chapter 10 - The Return to Overhead Systems.

Blackpool Corporation Transport ran the oldest and, by 1994, the only remaining street tramway in the country, using equipment mostly dating from the 19th century. The local council judged the system worth upgrading and this would be done as one contract with the replacement of the power supplies for the illuminations which were no longer meeting current safety regulations. The contract was awarded to BW in the summer - a century after the Company's first overhead job. The team in Chard were responsible for the overhead design and supply, and calculations on the whole system. This was a good chance to show what could be done. A range of fittings was designed using some from the BICC range bought back in 1972 and some new items developed using investment castings and tubing in stainless steel to counter the severe marine environment. After extensive type testing in the factory, the new equipment was erected at night, choosing positions between the existing poles, and then subsequently the old system removed, so that apart from a few weekend closures, the normal tram service was not affected. The new BW system proved to be a success, with a much reduced maintenance effort being needed. It also retained the overall styling of the original Victorian system - even many informed observers failed to notice that the system was all-new! The Blackpool contract had been stolen from under the noses of existing railway-type contractors, whose designs for light rail were derived from main line work, and had received criticism for the heavy look which was the result. BW was determined to promote a better image, going for aesthetically-pleasing designs, and this attitude was soon to bear fruit.

The West Midlands Metro between Birmingham and Wolverhampton, was to be built on the course of the old GWR line from Snow Hill. The lead contractor was Ansaldo, an Italian engineering concern and they appointed BW to work on the overhead design. The system involved 40 single track kilometres of overhead, all designed new, with extensive interfacing with the civil engineers, especially on the street-running portion of the line in Wolverhampton. Installation under BW supervision started in April 1997, and proceeded for the next 18 months. The first tram ran into the street in autumn 1998. The overhead was fairly heavy, owing to the need for large section copper wires, but the system overall was well praised for its looks and it performed well.

Work with Ansaldo had gone well, and the extension of the Manchester Metrolink to Salford Quays was the next project on the cards, and Ansaldo won again. The policy for 'good looking overhead' was welcomed by Manchester, whose original system had been much criticised, and BW won the contract, which involved extensive street running as well as a tricky tie-in operation with the existing lines. Unfortunately the work suffered financially with installation difficulties, notably the need to work at night to recover time lost in civil works delays. Contracts at Croydon and Nottingham, meanwhile, passed to French and German contractors respectively, before the financial pressures in Britain caused a temporary halt to new light rail schemes in 1998.

Twenty years after the ill-fated Advanced Passenger Trains, the west coast main line was once again considering tilting train technology. The Pendolino train was of Italian origins but BW's pantograph design still enjoyed unique approval status in Britain, and was selected for the trains, to be mounted onto an anti-tilt mechanism on the train roof. The BW unit featured a number of minor improvements from previously, and was designed to run at 140mph although other limitations restricted the trains to 125mph in service.

1999 was the year when the computer drawing systems overtook the traditional methods of pen and pencil. The older drawings in use were scanned onto computer format from the original paper or linen copies, and from then on would be dealt with like any other computer drawing. The number of computer stations in the Drawing Office increased, and the drawing boards were scrapped one by one. Finally the historic moment came just before the end of the year, when the last drawing board was removed from the design office. Drawing boards had served the Company well since the beginning, and for many of the older staff it was difficult to imagine life in Engineering without them.

Also in 1999 there was a new series of investments in the machine shop. It was always difficult to strike a balance between the low-volume specialised BW requirement and the high-volume capacity available from modern machines. The price of new machines had become so low, however, that much re-equipping of the shop could be done at economic rates. The older, hand-operated machines were moved into a spillover shop to one side of the site. Summer 1999 was quiet, however, and BW ran short of work. The new, private, Railtrack was cutting back on new projects, and several key foreign contracts were delayed. Once again, the Company was squeezed from the combined effects of export delays and the lack of a regular home market. There was little choice but to cut the workforce, and in June nineteen staff were made redundant. Once again BW made the front page of the Chard and Ilminster, but not this time for international successes. August was the quietest month for many years, and to ease the situation, two welders were lent to Stemmann to offset staff shortages there - a good example of cooperation between the two companies. On 11th August 1999 production was stopped for half an hour for staff to watch the eclipse of the sun, which would be 99% totality from Chard. Unfortunately, cloud obscured the show....

After 15 years of third rail design, it might be thought that all the possible configurations had been dealt with; but there was one style yet untouched - the special side-running two-pole system used in Canada. Attempts to gain work there had all come to naught because of the good connections between the Operator and the local manufacturer, Insul-8, but a proposed extension to the existing system in Vancouver gave a new opportunity. BW promoted hard its ability to handle all the engineering elements of such a contract, including attendance at a large show in Toronto. The prospective Client, Bombardier Transportation, was impressed, and BW won the contract - for 80km of rail, insulators, all parts and all design activities. Work was rapid and intense, for a whole new system had to be designed, developed, proven and approved within 8 months. The timescales were achieved, and rail was being installed on the new line in June 2000. To meet production requirements, the rail shop in Chard was put onto double shift, and a new machining facility developed to be able to give an output from the line of up to 40 metres per hour. The rail shop had some stable workload at last.

Photo 10.1 The new Blackpool overhead poles as installed by BW in 1995. Note the attractive finial and the pale upper paintwork, which was intended to assist in blending in with the surroundings.

Photo 10.2 The first overhead poles are erected at West Midlands Metro, 1997.

Photo 10.3 The first tram to Wolverhampton for many years - the test run in August 1998.

Photo 10.4 Andrew Grinter, Tony Larcombe and Nigel Potter lay out a copper dip-tank collector system on the paved area outside 'The Elms'.

Photo 10.5 In 2000 several staff reached their 25th years of employment with BW. On the extreme left is Bob Hindess, while receiving their awards are left to right: Peter Hoare, Gordon Down, Nigel Heselton, Brian Andrews, Tony Larcombe and Tony White, Managing Director.

Photo 10.6 Manchester Phase 2 extension overhead is complete here in 2000, showing centre poles with combined street lighting.

Photo 10.7 The Vancouver Skytrain system in February 2001. The conductor rails are arranged as a two-pole side-running system.

Photo 10.8 Site map in 2001. Since the 1961 view, the site has been truncated by the building of the Millfield road; a new Tapstone Road has been built, and the old Tapstone Lane incorporated into the BW site itself, with a gateway across the north end. Space Decks has a separate site but still has access past the former Denings building. The railway has gone, and the site vacant after a Bass warehouse has come and gone. Recently a Tesco supermarket has been built in this area.

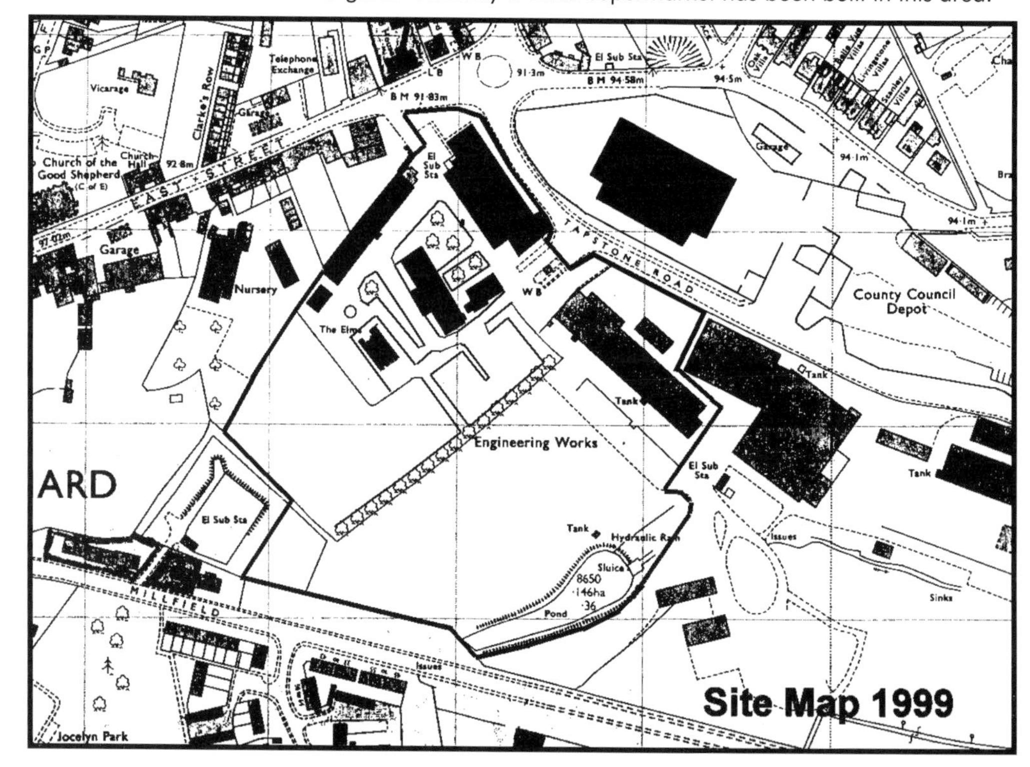

Chapter 11- The Third Century

The book so far has been written in the past tense, for it has dealt with events which are recorded in documents and photographs loosely categorised as 'archives'. More recent events are harder to talk about, and I believe strongly that a correct and balanced account can only be given fairly with the hindsight which comes with the passage of time. To try to detail developments of the last few years would not only be unfair, but it would run the risk of trespassing on individual emotions and potentially compromising projects which are in the early stages of development. For this reason I do not intend to give details, but merely to mention a few significant trends and large scale changes.

We are strongly part of the railway business, and here major changes are occurring as large conglomerates are forming out of much smaller organisations. What were once many different train building companies spread around the world, are now reduced to five major ones in the western hemisphere, with others in Japan and Korea, and further changes are likely. Very little train building capability remains in this country. Recent British train contracts have been won by organisations where the entire design and manufacturing operation is overseas, and to win business, we are having to fight more strongly on a global basis. At the same time, our independent ownership has allowed us to work with all the international groups and joint ventures without complication.

In Britain, the major rolling stock work involves steady replacement of the slam-door trains on the former southern region of Network Rail. This build has required many hundreds of sets of shoegear, and we have won the majority of this work, supplying to Alstom, Bombardier and Siemens for assembly onto the trains. With the Desiro trains built by Siemens, we have exported the shoegear to Germany, where they are mounted onto the trains, tested on the Wildenrath test track, and then return to England for service!

On the conductor rail side, our two world competitors have joined forces, and are actively bidding against us on international work. The market for conductor rail is opening in the USA, with both New York and Chicago operators interested in 'aluminum' rails for the future. To meet 'buy America' rules, a brand new production line is in operation at Transtech, supported by BW staff, producing trial rails. The new facility is a showpiece in terms of presentation but awaits economic orders in the Americas. A new monorail system in Kuala Lumpur is equipped with our collectors and aluminium rail system, and is a good example of a simple but effective raised monorail peoplemover in an urban environment. A major coup has been the provision of current collection equipment for the magnetic levitation Transrapid trains in Shanghai. This followed trial work at the test site in northern Germany, and forms a prestigious contract, in a German-dominated product. Also in Germany, we are supplying conductor rail to the S-Bahn in Berlin, with demand so intense that the rail shop has been working 24 hours per day. This output requires delivery by rail, so the production is taken to Bridgwater by road, and trans-shipped to railway wagons for the journey through the Channel Tunnel to Berlin.

Our work continues apace in East Asia, with extensions to the MRT's in both Singapore and Taipei, with BW supplying conductor rail and shoegear for the new projects, and there is potential work in mainland China.

Partial privatisation of London Underground is underway, but the detail plans for new rolling stock and track upgrading are still far from clear as the new organisations move to the start of their 30 year contracts. It is to be hoped, at least, that the new management will concentrate on whole life costs in their contract awards, for the long term benefit of the system.

We have the contract for the tramway in Dublin, and installation of the street overhead system is well advanced. We are using an installation team with staff drawn mainly from the Chard factory; it is working flexibility like this which gains much respect from our customers. For the first time, our work is including the complex and demanding job of surveying and negotiating the fixings to buildings, with lengthy and sometimes fractious discussions with local landowners and surveyors.

The British government attitude to urban light railways continues to fluctuate, and the great rush of projects forecast in the 1990's has failed to materialise. Currently only one new scheme is in prospect, a major extension to the Manchester Metrolink system. Other cities have feasibility schemes underway, but the chances of the projects coming to fruition seem slim. One such uncertain development is the Bristol Light Rail Project, which would consist of several routes around the city streets, and out to the suburbs. How appropriate it would be for Brecknell's to be involved again with such a project, over 100 years after the first time around! Alas, after several false starts over many years, this project is still in abeyance, and the BW marketing file continues to gather dust in 'The Elms' attic archives.

Changes continue on the Chard site. Space Decks have left, to move to a greenfield development in Chard, and their area at Old Town Mill is now occupied by Numatic, the vacuum cleaner manufacturer. The local council is reviving the concept of a right of way across the site in the form of a cycleway, and the way seems set for an exchange of land between BW and Numatic. This will result in a new boundary across the southern edge of the old Denings building and at last, after 66 years, BW will have a site totally to itself, with its own exclusive entrance, fully fenced and secure. Building maintenance continues to occupy our minds. The old Denings building has lasted well, but its age has prompted thoughts about demolition and rebuilding, perhaps on one of the fields. The main assembly hall is almost forty years old, and brings its own challenges, notably a colony of seagulls which have defied all reasonable attempts to move on. We continue to pursue the policy of steady sustainable development of the Works, retaining as much as possible the character of the site, and its areas of isolation and natural beauty.

Conclusions.

Brecknell, Willis is a remarkable firm. From the initial family beginnings it grew into an international company, then collapsed and has since returned to the level of a global organisation. Nevertheless it has retained its family atmosphere in a world where the condensing of companies into conglomerates has dominated the news.

The company remains private and continues to manufacture most of its products in its own factory, and retains its own engineering research and development department which is a major selling point to the world, developing new products for the future. It is undoubtedly true that if Henry Brecknell, Edward Munro or Arnold Willis were to return today, they would feel instantly at home. It continues to employ 140 directly, provides jobs indirectly for many more in supplier companies, and contributes significantly to the wealth of Chard and the surroundings. For the good of our employees, past, present and future, may the situation continue.

Photo 11.1 In 2001 aluminium rail was installed as part of a major track renewal at Brixton on the Victoria line of London Underground. This is the scene as the rails were being installed.

Photo 11.2 With the departure of Space Decks, the BW social club was reformed alone, and continues to run a series of trips and events every year. In July 2000 a team from BW entered the raft race at West Bay, and won! Left to right: Richard Parker, Phil Beadsworth, Les Hallett and Richard Whitefield.

Photo 11.3 An Alstom Citadis tram running on trial in Dublin, taking power from the BW overhead system.

Photo 11.4 The first Kuala Lumpur monorail train at the test track, 2001.

Photo 11.5 Aluminium conductor rail from Chard on its way from Bridgwater to Berlin via the Channel Tunnel in September 2003.

Photo 11.6 The Brecknell, Willis installation gang at Dublin, in February 2004 with their overhead line machinery and the trams in the background.

Photo 11.7 The Shanghai Transrapid magnetic levitation vehicle reaches 290mph on the way to the airport. BW shoegear is installed for collecting current from the track.

The Brecknell, Willis Comma.

Company names in Victorian times were usually formed from the surnames of the partners involved. If there were just two, then the names were separated by 'and' or '&' to form the name. With three or more, then commas were used to extend the series, thus "Brecknell, Munro and Rogers". This is fine for a small team of, say, solicitors, but for a larger firm employing many tens or hundreds of people the whole staff deserve a mention, and a much better impression is given if the suffix 'and Company' is used. This emphasises the team effort - the fact that the operation is more than just a few partners or directors, but is also the results of many people working together. The formal name, therefore, for this organisation is Brecknell, Willis and Company.

To shorten the name for common speech the 'and Company' may be dropped, but it would be quite wrong under these circumstances to say Brecknell & Willis - substituting the '&' for the comma has the effect of excluding the rest of the employees!
Hence Brecknell, Willis.

This, anyway, is the tradition. We have seen two other examples in this book where the organisation names have been constructed in the same way, and both with equally long associations - Dick, Kerr and Company and Beyer, Peacock and Company.

We use our comma with pride!

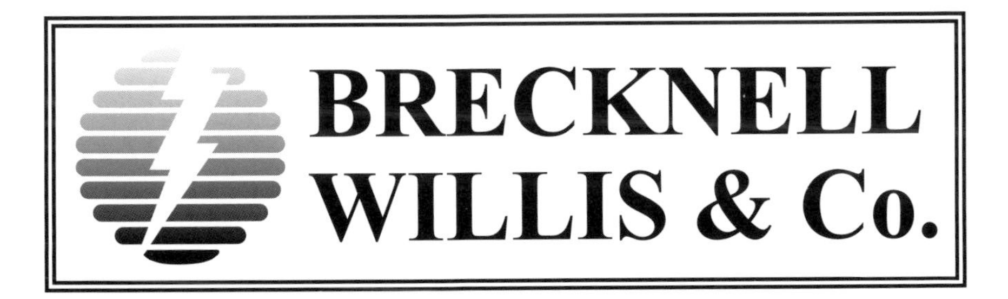

MP Middleton Press

Easebourne Lane, Midhurst, W Sussex. GU29 9AZ Tel: 01730 813169 Fax: 01730 812601
Email: sales@middletonpress.co.uk www.middletonpress.co.uk
If books are not available from your local transport stockist, order direct post free UK.

BRANCH LINES
Branch Line to Allhallows
Branch Line to Alton
Branch Lines around Ascot
Branch Line to Ashburton
Branch Lines around Bodmin
Branch Line to Bude
Branch Lines around Canterbury
Branch Lines around Chard & Yeovil
Branch Line to Cheddar
Branch Lines around Cromer
Branch Line to the Derwent Valley
Branch Lines to East Grinstead
Branch Lines of East London
Branch Lines to Effingham Junction
Branch Lines to Falmouth, Helston & St. Ives
Branch Line to Fairford
Branch Lines to Felixstow & Aldeburgh
Branch Lines around Gosport
Branch Line to Hayling
Branch Lines to Henley, Windsor & Marlow
Branch Line to Hawkhurst
Branch Line to Horsham
Branch Lines around Huntingdon
Branch Line to Ilfracombe
Branch Line to Kingsbridge
Branch Line to Kingswear
Branch Line to Lambourn
Branch Lines to Launceston & Princetown
Branch Lines to Longmoor
Branch Line to Looe
Branch Line to Lyme Regis
Branch Line to Lynton
Branch Lines around March
Branch Lines around Midhurst
Branch Line to Minehead
Branch Line to Moretonhampstead
Branch Lines to Newport (IOW)
Branch Lines to Newquay
Branch Lines around North Woolwich
Branch Line to Padstow
Branch Lines to Princes Risborough
Branch Lines to Seaton and Sidmouth
Branch Lines around Sheerness
Branch Line to Shrewsbury
Branch Line to Tenterden
Branch Lines around Tiverton
Branch Lines to Torrington
Branch Lines to Tunbridge Wells
Branch Line to Upwell
Branch Line to Wantage (The Wantage Tramway)
Branch Lines of West London
Branch Lines of West Wiltshire
Branch Lines around Weymouth
Branch Lines around Wimborne
Branch Lines around Wisbech

NARROW GAUGE
Austrian Narrow Gauge
Branch Line to Lynton
Branch Lines around Portmadoc 1923-46
Branch Lines around Porthmadog 1954-94
Branch Line to Southwold
Douglas to Port Erin
Douglas to Peel
Kent Narrow Gauge
Northern France Narrow Gauge
Romneyrail
Sierra Leone Narrow Gauge
Southern France Narrow Gauge
Sussex Narrow Gauge
Surrey Narrow Gauge
Swiss Narrow Gauge
Two-Foot Gauge Survivors
Vivarais Narrow Gauge

SOUTH COAST RAILWAYS
Ashford to Dover
Bournemouth to Weymouth
Brighton to Worthing
Dover to Ramsgate
Eastbourne to Hastings
Hastings to Ashford
Portsmouth to Southampton
Ryde to Ventnor
Southampton to Bournemouth

SOUTHERN MAIN LINES
Basingstoke to Salisbury
Crawley to Littlehampton
Dartford to Sittingbourne
East Croydon to Three Bridges
Epsom to Horsham
Exeter to Barnstaple
Exeter to Tavistock
London Bridge to East Croydon
Orpington to Tonbridge
Tonbridge to Hastings
Salisbury to Yeovil
Sittingbourne to Ramsgate
Swanley to Ashford
Tavistock to Plymouth
Three Bridges to Brighton
Victoria to Bromley South
Victoria to East Croydon
Waterloo to Windsor
Waterloo to Woking
Woking to Portsmouth
Woking to Southampton
Yeovil to Exeter

EASTERN MAIN LINES
Barking to Southend
Ely to Kings Lynn
Ely to Norwich
Fenchurch Street to Barking
Hitchin to Peterborough
Ilford to Shenfield
Ipswich to Saxmundham
Liverpool Street to Ilford
Saxmundham to Yarmouth
Tilbury Loop

WESTERN MAIN LINES
Banbury to Birmingham
Bristol to Taunton
Didcot to Banbury
Didcot to Swindon
Ealing to Slough
Exeter to Newton Abbot
Moreton-in-Marsh to Worcester
Newton Abbot to Plymouth
Newbury to Westbury
Oxford to Moreton-in-Marsh
Paddington to Ealing
Paddington to Princes Risborough
Plymouth to St. Austell
Princes Risborough to Banbury
Reading to Didcot
Slough to Newbury
St. Austell to Penzance
Swindon to Bristol
Swindon to Newport
Taunton to Exeter
Westbury to Taunton

MIDLAND MAIN LINES
St. Albans to Bedford
Euston to Harrow & Wealdstone
Harrow to Watford
St. Pancras to St. Albans

COUNTRY RAILWAY ROUTES
Abergavenny to Merthyr
Andover to Southampton
Bath to Evercreech Junction
Bath Green Park to Bristol
Bournemouth to Evercreech Junction
Brecon to Newport
Burnham to Evercreech Junction
Cheltenham to Andover
Croydon to East Grinstead
Didcot to Winchester
East Kent Light Railway
Frome to Bristol
Guildford to Redhill
Reading to Basingstoke
Reading to Guildford
Redhill to Ashford
Salisbury to Westbury
Stratford upon Avon to Cheltenham
Strood to Paddock Wood
Taunton to Barnstaple
Wenford Bridge to Fowey
Westbury to Bath
Woking to Alton
Yeovil to Dorchester

GREAT RAILWAY ERAS
Ashford from Steam to Eurostar
Clapham Junction 50 years of change
Festiniog in the Fifties
Festiniog in the Sixties
Festiniog 50 years of enterprise
Isle of Wight Lines 50 years of change
Railways to Victory 1944-46
Return to Blaenau 1970-82
SECR Centenary album
Talyllyn 50 years of change
Wareham to Swanage 50 years of change
Yeovil 50 years of change

LONDON SUBURBAN RAILWAYS
Caterham and Tattenham Corner
Charing Cross to Dartford
Clapham Jn. to Beckenham Jn.
Crystal Palace (HL) & Catford Loop
East London Line
Finsbury Park to Alexandra Palace
Holborn Viaduct to Lewisham
Kingston and Hounslow Loops
Lewisham to Dartford
Liverpool Street to Chingford
Mitcham Junction Lines
North London Line
South London Line
West Croydon to Epsom
West London Line
Willesden Junction to Richmond
Wimbledon to Beckenham
Wimbledon to Epsom

STEAMING THROUGH
Steaming through Cornwall
Steaming through the Isle of Wight
Steaming through Kent
Steaming through West Hants

TRAMWAY CLASSICS
Aldgate & Stepney Tramways
Barnet & Finchley Tramways
Bath Tramways
Brighton's Tramways
Bristol's Tramways
Burton & Ashby Tramways
Camberwell & W.Norwood Tramways
Clapham & Streatham Tramways
Croydon's Tramways
Derby Tramways
Dover's Tramways
East Ham & West Ham Tramways
Edgware and Willesden Tramways
Eltham & Woolwich Tramways
Embankment & Waterloo Tramways
Exeter & Taunton Tramways
Fulwell - Home to Trams, Trolleys and Buses
Great Yarmouth Tramways
Greenwich & Dartford Tramways
Hammersmith & Hounslow Tramways
Hampstead & Highgate Tramways
Hastings Tramways
Holborn & Finsbury Tramways
Ilford & Barking Tramways
Kingston & Wimbledon Tramways
Lewisham & Catford Tramways
Liverpool Tramways 1. Eastern Routes
Liverpool Tramways 2. Southern Routes
Liverpool Tramways 3. Northern Routes
Maidstone & Chatham Tramways
Margate to Ramsgate
North Kent Tramways
Norwich Tramways
Reading Tramways
Shepherds Bush & Uxbridge Tramways
Southend-on-sea Tramways
South London Line Tramways 1903-33
Southwark & Deptford Tramways
Stamford Hill Tramways
Twickenham & Kingston Tramways
Victoria & Lambeth Tramways
Waltham Cross & Edmonton Tramways
Walthamstow & Leyton Tramways
Wandsworth & Battersea Tramways

TROLLEYBUS CLASSICS
Bradford Trolleybuses
Croydon Trolleybuses
Derby Trolleybuses
Hastings Trolleybuses
Huddersfield Trolleybuses
Hull Trolleybuses
Maidstone Trolleybuses
Portsmouth Trolleybuses
Reading Trolleybuses

WATERWAY & SHIPPING
Kent and East Sussex Waterways
London to Portsmouth Waterway
Sussex Shipping - Sail, Steam & Motor
West Sussex Waterways

MILITARY BOOKS
Battle over Portsmouth
Battle over Sussex 1940
Blitz over Sussex 1941-42
Bombers over Sussex 1943-45
Bognor at War
East Ridings Secret Resistance
Military Defence of West Sussex
Military Signals from the South Coast
Secret Sussex Resistance
Surrey Home Guard

OTHER RAILWAY BOOKS
Industrial Railways of the South-East
South Eastern & Chatham Railways
London Chatham & Dover Railway
London Termini - Past and Proposed
War on the Line (SR 1939-45)